ARROW IN T

For a moment Lucie had felt herself so ready
and willing to surrender completely to Nat's
kiss that she could not speak. She could only
place her own hands on either side of his
head and draw his head closer. Their sanity
returned. All that was sensible and practical
in her broke through the dizzy haze of rapture.
She shook her head and pulled away, cupping
her burning cheeks with those hands which
had just now clung so passionately to him.
"No, Nat. This won't do."
"Darling, why?"
Immediately she had become a prey to all the
old tormenting fear that she would lose him—
the intense sadness that she had felt when he
had gone out of her life. Yet it was plain to
her he was not in love the way she was—that
to hold and kiss her, and make love to her
was not for him the beginning and the end of
things.

Arrow in the Heart

Denise Robins

CORONET BOOKS
Hodder Paperbacks Ltd., London

To my brother-in-law,
Jack O'Neill Pearson,
and to
Maria and Christine,
I dedicate this novel
about a boys' preparatory school.

Copyright © 1960 by Denise Robins
First published May 1960 by Hodder & Stoughton
Limited
Coronet edition 1963
Second impression 1972
Third impression 1975

Printed and bound in Great Britain for
Coronet Books, Hodder Paperbacks Limited.
St. Paul's House, Warwick Lane,
London, EC4P 4AH
By Cox & Wyman Ltd, London, Reading and Fakenham

ISBN 0 340 16038 1

ARROW IN THE HEART

I

WHEN the telephone bell rang during breakfast on that fateful morning in April, and Lucie sprang to her feet, blushing hotly, Margaret, her half-sister, knew for the first time that 'something was up'.

The two of them were sitting in the kitchen with the children, going through the usual routine of trying to make two small people eat properly, behave properly and stop making a din.

Up till then, Margaret—affectionately called 'Maggie'—had thought that Lucie looked a trifle pale and depressed. She had, of course, noticed lately that Lucie had been growing restless. It wasn't like her. She was usually a calm, contented sort of girl.

"Why," asked Maggie sharply, "should you suppose the phone to be for you?"

"I–I just think it is," stammered Lucie, and rushed out of the kitchen.

Maggie shrugged her shoulders and attended to her children: Timothy, aged seven, and Angela, still a baby of three. She adored them both, just as completely as she loved Dick, her husband, who was in the Navy, now in his ship somewhere in the Mediterranean.

Like all young women these days with small means and a family, Margaret Callow was kept busy. She wondered, sometimes, what she would have done without her half-sister's help. She also felt badly from time to time about Lucie being here, because she had given up a promising career to remain in this house in Hove and look after the family.

Dick had mentioned in his last letter that it was time Lucie was, so to speak, set free. Not that she had in any way been forced to stay an unhappy prisoner. She had volunteered to throw up her nursing profession when Margaret had had that serious operation a year ago. The situation had been so hopeless then. Margaret had had complications. Lucie just had to return home and stay. It was the only home she had known since their parents died, soon after Margaret's marriage.

At one time Lucie had been convinced that her heart lay in

a nursing career. She had gone away to train in a big London hospital. At the end of her second year, the catastrophe of Margaret's serious illness had put an end to Lucie's prospects of becoming a nurse. It was now nearly eleven months since she had left the hospital. Dick knew that his wife was well and strong again and could cope with the family. Margaret knew it, too. But she was not quite prepared for the blow which descended on her this morning when Lucie came back from that telephone call.

Margaret, who knew her so well, was instantly aware of a trace of guilt—as well as excitement—on Lucie's face.

"What's up with you?" Margaret asked, eyeing her.

Then Lucie blurted out:

"Oh, Maggie, that call *was* for me. I think I've landed a job!"

The elder girl, who had been dipping baby Angela's finger of toast into a boiled egg, dropped the spoon with a clatter. Angela immediately grabbed it and put it in her mouth and sucked it happily.

Lucie added:

"I didn't tell you until I knew I was going for the interview, but now I am."

"Well!" exclaimed Margaret, a trifle huffily, "I must say you've kept this very quiet."

But she could not help giving Lucie a smile. The child (she always thought of Lucie as that, because she was ten years younger than Margaret who had now reached what she considered the great age of thirty-two) looked so pretty this morning with that flush on her heart-shaped face. Usually she was without colour. She never tanned much and had an exceptionally pale skin. Being short-sighted, she wore horn-rimmed glasses, behind which there shone two very beautiful eyes, more green than blue, under those long heavy lashes so often found in short-sighted people. Lucie Reed was what the French call *petite*. Her movements were quick and graceful. She had an exceptionally slender waist which was her chief beauty. But she had missed being really beautiful because of that tip-tilted nose and rather wide mouth. She had fair, brown, silky hair which she wore in a little bun. It gave her an old-fashioned air. Without her glasses she looked a mere schoolgirl compared with her half-sister who was as plump as Lucie was thin, and already 'matronly'.

Lucie spoke in a rather guilty voice:

"I hardly dare tell you, but I shall have to leave you on the first of May, Maggie darling; if all goes well at my interview, and I don't see why it shouldn't."

Breakfast over, Margaret turned the children out into the small garden at the back of the villa and smoked a cigarette while Lucie had made her confession.

She had not meant to go off until the end of that year, she said, but lately she had felt that she was no longer really needed here and she did so want a job and life of her own. She could not bear to be dependent on Maggie and Dick any longer, even though she was working for them. But she had decided that she could not face returning to hospital. Perhaps she had never really had a true vocation, but after a year's absence she had found that the nurses who had been probationers with her had gone on ahead and that it would really mean starting all over again, with strangers. Then she had seen the advertisment. Keynwood Hall School wanted a matron with some hospital experience, to work under supervision, starting the beginning of the summer term.

Now Margaret pricked up her ears and looked attentively at Lucie.

"Keynwood Hall! But that's where Nat Randall was a master!"

Now Lucie coloured violently.

"That's right. Still is there, presumably. He was on the resident staff."

"But you must be *cracked*!" exclaimed Maggie. "I thought that the last person you'd want to see was *Nat*."

Lucie stared at the teacup which she was holding. She poured herself out yet another. She felt thirsty and madly excited.

How wrong Maggie was! Nat wasn't the last person whom she wanted to see, but the *only* one. From the time that she had noticed the advertisement, she had felt a little light-headed, she told herself wryly. The very name of Nat's school had aroused such bitter-sweet memories.

"I presume you must have got over that affair or you wouldn't be applying for the job," she heard her half-sister observe.

Lucie gulped. That wasn't true either. She *hadn't* got over it; for since writing her letter to the Headmaster applying for the job, she had continually thought how wonderful it would be to live under the same roof as Nat . . . to see him again . . .

breathe the same air . . . hear his voice. She realised how very much she wanted him back in her life. She had done her duty by Margaret and Dick and the children, but it was monotonous here and she was wasted, too, because she had that two years' nursing experience which she could offer to the little boys at Keynwood and earn some money as well. Her small nephew attended day-school. Maggie could manage Angela alone.

Lucie knew that she had always suffered from having too much heart. The thought of Nat and that 'affair', as Maggie called it, of last summer crowded back into her mind. Why had she of all people to fall in love with *him*? With a young man who was hard as iron. Charming . . . oh, dear life! how charming Nat Randall used to be! . . . in an indescribable way. He seemed to get under one's skin immediately he took one's hands and said 'Hello'. Good-looking, clever, he taught English and History at school. He had a way of making a woman feel that she was important to him. Whether she was or not didn't matter. His charm, Lucie thought, was like a magnet drawing one to him irresistibly against one's will. Not that it was against hers.

She had met him at a dance in Brighton. After a second glance at Nat and their first dance, she had known that she was like the girl in *My Fair Lady*; she could have 'danced all night' . . . with Nat.

But at times during their association, even when things seemed to be going with a swing and life was one big thrill for Lucie, he used to draw away—remove himself completely from her orbit. She would feel then as though she had been flung outside in the cold void and left by him there to shiver.

She hadn't seen or heard of Nat for about nine months now. But sitting here in Maggie's kitchen she could almost hear his familiar rich, rather lazy voice, saying:

"Ring me up some time, *Santa Lucia*, and when I can get away I'll come and take you out. You dance very prettily, and its such an agreeable change to dance instead of looking after a lot of horrid noisy little boys."

He had given her that lovely and rather foolish nickname *Santa Lucia* which nobody else had ever thought of (or would again). Saint Lucie . . . it suited her, he used to laugh. She was such a good little girl! Rather too good and prim to be amusing for long to Nat, perhaps. Yet she had wanted to be all things to him.

There had never been anything definite between Nat and Lucie. He had taken her out from time to time. They seemed to have grown close. She, who had never been in love before, had learned what it was to tremble when she heard that he was coming to take her out; to feel, with ridiculous exaggeration, *ready to die* when he kissed her hand at parting or told her that she was the 'sweetest small person in the world'.

Just that sort of thing and nothing more—then suddenly he had gone away. Perhaps he had never guessed what an effect he had on her, she thought bitterly.

Margaret was flinging questions at her. She tried to stop thinking about Nat and tried to answer her half-sister, explain her side of it.

She was twenty-two, nearly twenty-three, she said. She felt that Keynwood wanted a matron with nursing experience under supervision, she could qualify for the job. One of her girl-friends had become a matron in a boys' preparatory school, starting with four pounds a week and her keep, and was now getting five pounds. That wasn't bad, and there were the lovely long holidays, and, Lucie added with a rather ingratiating smile at her half-sister, "I can come home then and help you with Tim and Angela. You'll really need me in the summer when Dick's on leave."

"Will you tell the Head that you're a friend of Nat?"

Lucie bit her lip.

"I'll see."

She had gone to Keynwood once, for a Sports' Day, last summer, as Nat's guest. She had met and liked Hugh Friern enormously, just from the little she had seen of him. Nat always said that he was a 'great chap'; but she could not at the moment decide whether or not she would mention to anyone about her previous association with the History and English master.

Now Maggie stared at Lucie's small pink face. She recognised that firm tilt to the pointed chin, that determined way in which Lucie compressed her lips. She had a strong will behind her shy façade and all her gentleness. She was really full of character. Like their father used to be, Margaret reflected.

"It still seems odd to me that you want to get mixed up with Nat Randall again," at length Margaret observed aloud.

That brought a torrent of words from Lucie. She had never

been 'mixed up with Nat'. They had only been great friends.
He had only kissed her once after a dance. Maggie didn't
know, etc., etc.

"But you were in love with him and you lost a whole stone
after he stopped seeing you. Don't I know it!" exclaimed
Margaret.

Lucie took off her spectacles and wiped them. She blinked
her long lashes and admitted that she *had* cared more for Nat
than she ought to have done.

"Well I thought he was a cad—although, I admit, absolutely
charming!" said Margaret.

Nothing would induce Lucie to agree that Nat was a cad.

"It would be absurd," she said, loyally, "if a man had to
propose marriage to every girl he took out. Besides, perhaps I
played my cards badly."

And she reminded Maggie of Marta, an old school-friend
of Lucie's, who was as glamorous and as go-ahead as Lucie
always wished herself to be. Marta always said that one must
have courage and not hang about in the background. *One
should go out and get one's man.* Well—now Lucie was going to
Keynwood Hall, and if she finally got the job there she would
make certain this time that Nat didn't escape.

Then Margaret roared with laughter.

"You are priceless, Lucie darling. Such a demure mouse at
times. But Dick always said he believed you were the sort who
would one day get what she wanted."

Lucie joined in the laughter. Then she grew serious. She
hadn't got what she wanted yet, she thought sadly.

After Nat had faded out of her life she had wished passionately that she could behave like Marta who had fallen in love
with a rich young man in the Foreign Office, Guy Traill by
name. Guy had been posted to the Sudan and Marta had got
herself invited out to Khartoum—deliberately pursuing the
man she wanted. Yes, and she had come back with his ring on
her finger.

For an instant Lucie shut her eyes and instead of Maggie's
sunny little kitchen with all the unwashed dishes and the dis-
order the children had left, and Maggie's plump face and
figure, she saw Nat. That amazingly sculptured handsome
face of his; that lithe graceful body. She recalled one especial
night outside this very house, in his car, when he had kissed
her.

"I'm really growing too fond of you," he had whispered against her lips. *Too fond?* Was it because he cared for her but didn't want to get married that he had walked out of her life? She didn't know. But she was quite sure that life beckoned her down the road that led back to Nat. She must *make* him fall in love with her . . . feel those lips burning against hers again . . . and be made to forget the days and nights when she had broken her heart because the phone never rang, and Nat never wrote. It was an obsession with her now.

She went up to her bedroom—reproaching herself for the untidiness. She must pull herself together and learn to be neater—more orderly. She remembered, grimacing, how one Sister in hospital had criticised her in this respect. Down on her knees she dropped, on the carpet, pulled out the bottom drawer and found a box. In that box, carefully treasured, were so many souvenirs of that long lovely summer in Sussex when she had seen so much of Nat. A snapshot, showing him sitting in a boat on a lake which they had visited. Nat in shorts, and sports shirt. She had been so deliriously happy that afternoon; he had been trying to teach her to row and laughed at her puny efforts. Later, under the shade of a beech-tree, they had sat together, eating cherries which she had bought for the picnic. She remembered how he had leaned toward her, touching her lips with the tip of a finger and whispering:

"Cherry-ripe . . . sweet, generous mouth. You look like a child, stained with the fruit-juice. It is enchanting."

Those murmured words had thrilled her. And she had lived as though under a warm, passionate spell. Yet never sure, once he left her, that it had not all been a dream.

She sifted through her treasures; found a china cat he had bought her on the Brighton front because she admired it. A bunch of violets, long since faded and dried—kept because he had given them to her. A menu. A theatre programme. 'Just like a Victorian,' Lucie thought emotionally, 'I have kept everything connected with Nat. And now I am going to be with him again. *Oh, Nat, Nat, love me this time and never let me go!*'

2

Keynwood Hall had at one time been what the estate agents call 'a desirable Georgian residence', but when it became a school it had been considerably built on to and, perhaps, spoiled. But it was still a fine building.

On that April afternoon, standing on the portico—the taxi from Horsham station had just dropped her—Lucie tried to concentrate on the fact that she had applied for the job of matron and been granted an interview.

This was it.

Now to face the Headmaster, Mr. Friern. But Lucie kept thinking about Nat and the day she had spent with him here ten months ago. It was wildly exciting to think that this was where he worked (or so she hoped). It really would be a blow if she found that he had moved to another school.

The place had a deserted air today. All was quiet. No little boys rushing around; all were home for the 'hols'.

A gardener was cutting the lawn in front of the Headmaster's study. There were some beautiful flowers in the herbaceous border. To the right lay the starkness of the playing fields, and one could just see the sun glistening on the swimming pool.

Keynwood wasn't a very well-known prep school, but it was 'coming on', and fast gaining distinction.

Lucie rang the bell and stood with her heart fluttering, hoping that she looked all right; that Mr. Friern would like her. She had had a battle with Margaret about her clothes. Because it was a warm day, Margaret had suggested that Lucie put on a summery floral dress with loose jacket, but she had chosen a well-worn grey flannel suit with a white shirt, and bought herself a grey felt hat. She hoped it would make her look 'schooly' and that her glasses would encourage Mr. Friern to believe that she really was 'matronly'.

The bell was not answered for a long time, because, Lucie supposed, of a depleted staff during holiday time. Finally, Lucie was admitted by a tall willowy girl who was rather a startling sight for any school. She wore slacks with an emerald green, boat-necked jersey showing a fine throat. She had reddish waving hair brushed to one side, and heavily-lidded, light blue eyes. She would have been beautiful but for her thin mouth and a narrow jaw which gave her what Shakespeare would have called 'a lean and hungry look'. Lucie didn't find her voice very pleasant; it was too high-pitched.

"Yes?" queried the girl, staring at the caller.

Immediately she made Lucie nervous. She stammered that her name was Miss Reed and that she had an appointment with the Headmaster.

The light, cold eyes gave a flicker of interest. The tall girl then shrugged as though to dismiss Lucie and the whole affair from her mind.

"I don't know anything about you, but I expect my father does. I'm Barbara Friern."

Now Lucie remembered . . . she had seen Miss Friern on that Sports' Day last summer. Nat had pointed her out and told Lucie that everyone called her 'Barbie'. Lucie remembered something else Nat had said . . . that Barbie Friern was extremely self-centred but quite dangerously attractive to men. He admitted, however, that he did not find her so. But Lucie felt that Nat would never admit to being attracted by any girl other than the one he was with at the moment. That was his 'gambit'.

He had also told Lucie that Barbie was twenty-four, and all out to find a husband. So far she hadn't achieved it, which made her a 'menace' (one of Nat's favourite words). Barbie apparently used to leave Keynwood from time to time to take odd secretarial jobs abroad, and several times had worked in Geneva. But since the school had been so enlarged, she had been persuaded to stay at home and help her parents.

Miss Friern certainly had a way of making one feel insignificant, thought Lucie, as she walked meekly after Barbara into the Headmaster's study.

"Wait here, I'll go and find my father," said Miss Friern languidly, and left Lucie alone.

Lucie began to feel—as she imagined many little boys must feel when they were summoned to this inner sanctum—horribly nervous. Blankly she stared at the big desk, the important revolving chair, a pile of exercise books. The walls were lined with shelves of scholastic literature; there were endless photographs: of boys, little and big, past and present, football groups, cricket-elevens—weddings! (Weddings of 'old boys', Lucie presumed.)

In particular, her attention was attracted to two photographs in a double leather frame which stood on the Head's desk. One in colour, of the girl she had just seen . . . Barbara Friern . . . looking beautiful and sophisticated in a tight-fitting cocktail-dress. The other, a thin, rather sour-looking woman who wore a fringe. This Lucie imagined to be Mrs. Friern.

Then the door opened. The Headmaster came in. Lucie stood up. She saw a tall, angular, slightly bald man with big horn-rimmed glasses. He had a hatchet-shaped, clever face with eyes that were shrewd but kindly. Hugh Friern looked what he was. A man without conscious charm, yet essentially nice. The clean-looking English sporting type one associates with spotless white flannels and a day's sport. He greeted the young girl cordially:

"Miss Reed, I presume?"

He had a rich voice and a warm handclasp which reassured Lucie. She could see that he hadn't recognised her as the girl Nat Randall had once brought to a Keynwood Sports' Day.

He sat down in his revolving chair and with a sweeping gesture (with which she was to grow familiar) moved everything on the desk, spreading out the papers, the ink-pot, the paper-weights, the books, clearing his throat, blinking—a man who obviously had a lot on his mind.

"Always busy," he said with his genial smile. "Even when the boys are not here, not a moment to spare, preparing for next term."

"I can imagine," Lucie nodded.

"Let me see, you told me on the phone that your age is twenty-two. That did strike me as being rather young but you seem to have had two years in hospital, and of course you wouldn't be required to take absolute control because my wife was a Red Cross nurse in the last war—so you would refer all serious matters to her."

Lucie told him that she quite understood, and tried to concentrate on what he was saying; yet every nerve in her body was aching to ask him if Nat was still the History and English master here at Keynwood.

Mr. Friern regarded her over the rim of his glasses.

"You *have* had nursing experience, haven't you?" he asked dubiously.

Lucie assured him that was so and that she was a serious, practical person who had dealt with young people at home as well as in a children's ward in the hospital for a whole year. She finally convinced him that she knew what she was talking about. He began to tell her what her duties here comprised.

Stella, his wife, he said, would have been here to talk to her but was away for two nights, staying with her mother whom she was moving into a new hotel. Most unfortunate, but it was essential, Mr. Friern said, that he should fix up a matron at once. The one they had expected had let them down at the last moment. He wanted to feel the staff problems were settled before term began. And that Lucie—if she came—would remain. He did not like changes in the staff. It was bad for the boys. Miss Reed would have to help look after their clothes, and baths, and with serving the meals. She must pay particular attention to the seven- and eight-year-olds. She would be busy all the morning but off in the afternoons till tea-time. She would breakfast and lunch with the boys and eat with the resident staff at night in Mr. Friern's private dining-room.

"We like the staff to feel that they are all one happy family," Mr. Friern added, and gave Lucie that warm smile which helped her to understand why he was a success. He wasn't at all frightening, really. He kept an astute finger on the pulse of things. Nothing would escape those bland blue eyes, but he was fundamentally a kind, endearing type.

He discussed other things with Lucie, such as keeping a guard on the health of the boys in general, and mending their clothes. She could have every other Sunday off, and a half-day once a week. Her salary would be two hundred pounds a year to start with.

"What I would like," he ended, "would be for you to work up to taking complete control, so that finally my wife would have less to do with that side of school-life here."

Lucie nodded.

"I'm sure I'll be able to manage, Mr. Friern."

"Then I don't see why we shouldn't give you a trial, if your references are satisfactory . . ." He coughed . . . "I would like a term's trial, if you don't mind ? You have a quiet way with you which I like and I can well believe that you are fond of children. I don't think you'd be unhappy here. We have an excellent residential staff including Miss Day, who teaches Geography and most subjects in the first form. Then there's our excellent

Languages master, Geoffrey Mallow who also takes sports, Mr. Randall, the History and English master. I myself teach Maths and Science."

Somehow Lucie managed to quell the leaping of her heart; to bite hard on her lip with sheer joy and excitement when she heard that cherished name.

So Nat was still here!

What on earth would he say when he knew she was to be the new matron? She could only pray, passionately, that he would be glad as well as astonished. And now it seemed that she really had landed the job because Mr. Friern asked her to report for duty on the first of May and said that he would like a letter from her at once, confirming the appointment. Then— could he have suitable references?

Lucie blurted out the name and rank of her naval brother-in-law, which she felt would be impressive, and the vicar of the church in Hove where Margaret and all of them at home worshipped. She also said that Mr. Friern could write to the hospital matron under whom she had trained. Now she could not resist adding:

"Actually, Mr. Randall knows me—and my sister. I came to Sports' Day at Keynwood with him last summer."

The Head beamed.

"Splendid, splendid. Well—I think it will all be very satisfactory. I'll tell my wife, and she'll look forward to meeting you in due course."

Lucie rose. She had put on a pair of glasses with one weak hinge; they slipped and fell off. It was rather a pity because she could see the Head's expression become doubtful again as he looked at her. People thought she looked so much younger without those glasses.

Quickly she stuck them on her nose again. Mr Friern said no more but stood up and suggested that his daughter, Barbara, should show Lucie over the school.

Lucie thanked him meekly although she felt it might not be altogether a pleasure to have Miss Friern for a guide. But a few moments later she was walking alone with Barbie down the long polished corridor into the boys' class-rooms, then up a staircase to the dormitories—which were comfortable-looking rooms, she thought—with six beds to a room. Miss Friern on this tour volunteered a brief laconic explanation of each part visited. Lucie could see that she was bored both with the school and with her, and soon became aware that she was not likely to find a bosom friend in the Head's good-looking daughter. But Lucie didn't care. She didn't care about anything except that Nat was still here.

After they had gone through the gym and seen the bathrooms and showers, and Lucie had been shown her own little room at the top of the house (it looked snug and well-furnished, and had a radiator, which pleased her because she always felt the cold,) she grew suddenly bolder. She decided to boast of the fact that she knew Mr. Randall.

At once, Barbara Friern's face changed. She swung round and looked at Lucie with interest.

"Oh—you know the famous Nat, do you?"

"Is he famous?" Lucie laughed weakly.

"Our Bright Boy. Pin-up Boy Number 1. I think he's fascinating."

Lucie felt then what she discovered later to be a fact—that Barbara Friern was hopelessly in love with Nat. Lucie was at once conscious of jealousy. She wondered if Nat had grown fond of Barbara. She also knew that she would have to be careful what she did and said where Miss Friern was concerned. She was more guarded in her answers now when Barbara questioned her about her friendship with Nat. She mentioned only casually that she had met him once or twice, and that was all; whereupon Barbie seemed to lose interest.

Once back in the front hall, Lucie had intended to ask if she could get a bus to Horsham station and save the taxi money, when a small sports-car rolled up, and a tall young man sprang from it.

Miss Friern said:

"Oh, what's *he* doing here?" and added, "It's Geoffrey Mallow, one of our masters."

Lucie remembered Mr. Friern telling her about Geoffrey Mallow. He had said some rather nice things about him, including the fact that he was very keen on cricket (he coached the boys) and that his hobby was Natural History.

He saw the two girls and greeted Miss Friern, who looked at him through her lashes and drawled:

"What brings you here, Geoff?"

"Business with your father," he said. "I've just got back from the Italian Alps. I took a walking holiday there this year. Quite glorious. Found some marvellous specimens."

"I must say you've got yourself a good tan," said Barbie enviously.

He glanced at Lucie and Barbara introduced them.

"Our future matron, Miss Reed."

Mr. Mallow shook hands with Lucie. It was the sort of firm handshake that she liked. It gave one confidence. He had a look of decision; an inner power, somehow, with his athletic frame, well-poised head, and determined manner. The brown face was rugged but not unhandsome. Too strong a jaw-line, perhaps. His rough chestnut hair was close-cropped. But his eyes were arresting, very bright hazel. Geoffrey Mallow had a penetrating way of looking at one—as though right through to the soul. It made Lucie feel uncomfortable, yet in a flash led her to believe that she could trust Geoffrey Mallow. Having shaken hands with her and muttered a welcome, he strode abruptly away and left the girls standing there alone. Barbara looked after him and laughed dryly.

"Same old Geoff. Confirmed bachelor. Uninterested in females. Loves only his old fauna and flora."

"He has kind eyes," Lucie said.

Miss Friern gave what Lucie thought to be a scathing look.

"Kind! What an awful word. I'm afraid mere kindness doesn't interest *me*. It can be such a bore."

'Yes,' Lucie thought, 'you'd be more interested in Nat's type. *He* isn't always kind. He's rather a devil. Don't I know it!'

Once again Lucie was about to ask Barbara for a bus time-table when the tall, grey-flannelled Mr. Mallow darted out of the house again and called to her personally:

"Miss . . . er . . . Reed."

"Yes?" she asked, surprised.

"The Head tells me you have a train to catch. I shall be only half an hour with him and if you like to wait I'll drive you to the station. Where are you going?"

"Hove," Lucie said.

"That's in the opposite direction to my home," he said, "so I regret that I can't take you all the way."

"It doesn't matter at all," Lucie replied. "The station will be fine."

Waiting for Mr. Mallow, Lucie wandered in the sunshine round the Head's private garden. Finally she went indoors again and found her way to the common-room where she imagined she would sit at times with the others on the staff.

Here the walls and the carpet were green. The furniture was comfortable and modern, of a lightish wood. There was a well-stocked book-case, a radio, and the usual framed school 'groups' half covering the walls.

Lucie went up to one of these photographs and suddenly picked out that particular face which had so persistently haunted her. Nat, sitting with folded arms, surrounded by a circle of pupils.

How sickening, Lucie thought, that her heart should lurch like that, just at the sight of that handsome face. His lips bore that little twisted smile that she had so often seen. Suddenly she did not know whether she had been mad to come here and surrender herself to his spell again, or if she was fiercely glad because she was so soon to re-enter his life.

Was he close friends with Barbara Friern nowadays? Lucie recalled that during most of her association with Nat, Barbie was away in Geneva where she had a secretarial job. But now he must see her every day. She was beautiful and amusing to men. During her talk just now with Lucie, she had called Nat 'Pin-up Boy Number 1'. *Her Pin-up Boy, perhaps?*

Lucie heard the sound of an engine revving, and hurried out to find the Languages master already at the wheel in his sports-car, waiting for her.

"Sorry, I didn't know you were ready," Lucie said breathlessly, and climbed in beside the driver.

"Quite all right," Geoffrey replied curtly.

As they turned out of the gates of Keynwood, Lucie ventured to remark that it was a gorgeous school and that she was lucky to have secured the matron's job.

He glanced at her sideways.

"I'm rather surprised you have."

"Why?"

"You look so young," he said, "but I don't doubt you've got the necessary qualifications!"

"Mr. Friern seemed to think so," said Lucie proudly. "Tell me about the rest of the staff, would you Mr. Mallow?"

"Oh, I think everybody's very nice," he said in a non-committal way.

"I'm a bit nervous," she confessed.

He seemed to sense her lack of confidence then, because his manner changed and as they drove along towards Horsham he adopted a more friendly attitude. Even a pitying one, Lucie thought, as though he knew that she had let herself in for something at Keynwood.

"Communal life, such as one leads in a school, isn't always as simple as one might suppose," he said. "You're apt to get absorbed into it and regimented like the boys, so you lose a certain amount of individuality which I find regrettable. I think it's better to lead a life on one's own if and when one can. When I'm off duty, I always try to get out alone."

"I understand," Lucie nodded, "and I shall do the same."

He gave a rather grim laugh.

"You'll have to battle for it. There are always those who want to include you in their lives and pursuits, and it is difficult to get out of saying 'yes' without appearing rude. I'm afraid I'm rather unpopular at times because I like to buzz off by myself. I like to hunt for rare species of orchids or such-like. I won't ramble around on these blessed picnics or go to the flicks with the others. Not that I don't like a theatre occasionally—I do. But I hate being dragged there by people."

"Isn't it good to make personal friends?" Lucie ventured.

"My personal friends are outside the school," he said (she thought rather coldly,) but instantly, as though sorry for being ungracious, he gave her the sort of smile that lit up his rugged face. "That sounds anti-social. I don't mean it to be," he added.

"I think it all depends," Lucie said, "on whether the rest of the staff appeal to you. There is a resident mistress, isn't there?"

"Yes," he said, "Miss Day . . . Beryl Day. We all call her Berry. She's a good sort but she'll have you in tow in no time if you're not careful. She belongs to all kinds of sects and societies and she'll drag you out to the lot if you're weak-willed."

"Don't scare me," Lucie begged him.

Then of course she couldn't resist the mention of *that* name.

"I have already met Mr. Randall—that is, sometime back," she found herself stuttering.

Geoffrey Mallow acknowledged this information by a nod of the head, then shut up like a clam. It wasn't difficult for Lucie to guess that he had no particular liking for Nat Randall. She could imagine that the two men were poles apart. Nat was an extrovert, the Languages master a withdrawn, rather difficult young man with that touch of bluntness that made him seem less charming on the surface than he might be, perhaps, underneath. By the time they reached Horsham station, she felt that she might grow to like and respect him. But he didn't make her girlish heart flutter.

When they reached the station, he smiled at her nicely, wished her luck and said he would see her on the first of May.

"Let me know if I can be of any help any time," he added.

Then Lucie caught her train to Hove and forgot him.

When Stella Friern returned to Keynwood, her husband informed her with some pride that he had engaged a new matron.

Mrs. Friern, removing a scarf from a neck which had grown scrawny for one barely fifty, eyed her husband out of the corners of her eyes. Her expression was one of perpetual doubt and worry. She said:

"Well, I think that was a bit dangerous, wasn't it—without me to judge?"

The Headmaster, who had been in the middle of answering a letter from a very difficult parent, was himself a trifle short-tempered this evening. Usually tranquil and long-suffering, he snapped:

"I really do not see why you should question my judgment, my dear. I count myself a psychologist."

Mrs. Friern twisted her lips. That was a habit he deplored. He knew that it meant that she was doubting again. He was very fond of Stella. They had been married for twenty-five years. She was five years his senior. She had a good brain which he admired and he appreciated the fact that she worked hard for the good of the school—sometimes too hard, which reduced her to a state of nervous tension. In Hugh Friern's opinion people running schools shouldn't have 'nervous tension', neither should they become a prey to all the anxieties which must necessarily at times beset those in charge of the young. Sometimes he asked himself why human beings changed so dismally over the years. Stella had never been pretty, but good-looking, with Barbara's wonderful hair. Her lips hadn't seemed so thin then nor did they twist in that aggravating way that indicated her disbelief. She had let her once-fine complexion coarsen. The red of her hair had faded. She dressed badly. He knew this, although he could not have made a single suggestion as to how she should alter her appearance. He only knew that she had become the one type of woman he had hoped she would never be. A dowdy, difficult 'school-marm'. But because he was a good man and deeply devoted, he tried not to quarrel with her. He had to make the same effort with his daughter. She had all the beauty and glamour that her mother lacked but her nature was hard and self-seeking and he was well aware of it.

He said with patience:

"Lucie Reed is an exceptionally nice girl if I know one."

"What age?"

"A bit young," said Hugh Friern and turned a slightly guilty face away from his wife when he remembered what a child the new matron looked, "but she'll do. She has good references and common sense, and she won't be one of these 'Miss know-alls', who irritate you so much, Stella. She'll be easy and pleased to work under you. You've just got to take what you can get these days."

"Oh, well," said Mrs. Friern shrugging, "I'm glad we're settled."

"How did you find your mother?"

"Difficult, as usual. She had a show-down with the proprietor of the last hotel she was in and I can see she'll soon have another in *this* place and I shall be moving her again."

'Never to Keynwood, I hope,' was the thought that sprang to the Headmaster's mind but remained unspoken.

Mrs. Friern went in search of her daughter. Secretly she shared her husband's opinion that Barbie was a disappointment and a constant threat to their peace, but she thought that the girl had seemed more settled lately. Of course Stella knew why; it was because Nat Randall was here.

She found Barbie in her own bedroom and asked if she had seen the new matron whom Hugh had just engaged.

Barbie yawned and nodded, and said that she thought Miss Reed rather an insignificant little person and much too baby-faced.

"Oh dear!" sighed Stella. "Too young, I suppose. I knew your father wasn't a judge of women. He ought to have waited for me. He said he didn't think I'd be back tonight and he ought to get on with it. Is she going to cause trouble, Barbie?"

"I think you'll be able to deal with her, Mummy," said the girl. Then after a pause, added: "She knows Nat."

"Don't tell me she's one of *his* girl-friends," began Mrs. Friern.

Do not affix postage stamps if posted in Gt. Britain, Channel Islands or Northern Ireland

Postage will be paid by licensee

BUSINESS REPLY SERVICE
LICENCE NO. KE 2450

CORONET ROMANCE CLUB

St. Paul's House

Warwick Lane

LONDON

EC4B 4HB

Barbara broke in:

"I can assure you she isn't. She isn't at all attractive or his type."

"Who is?" muttered Mrs. Friern. "But I'm glad she's plain. Attractive matrons can cause a lot of trouble and I don't trust Nat a *yard*, much as I like him."

"I wish *I* didn't trust him," said Barbie in a bitter voice.

"What did you say, dear?"

"Oh, nothing," said Barbie with a short laugh and walked out of the room.

3

Lucie remembered Geoffrey again that same evening while she had supper with Maggie. They had a chance to talk over the cup of tea, once the children were in bed. Excitedly, she told her half-sister all about the interview, and Geoffrey Mallow's name came into it.

"He sounds nice," said Maggie.

"Well, with Nat there, I shan't be interested in Mr. Mallow," said Lucie, grinning.

Margaret twisted her lips.

"Well, it's your own life; but I warn you, Lucie, you'll have to be careful, living under the same roof with a man you've once been so crazy about."

But Lucie felt no fear—only excitement.

"I shall get on. Mr. Mallow gave me one or two good tips on school life and I'm going to follow Marta's advice and go right out to make Nat my slave before I've finished."

Margaret giggled.

"Honestly, Lucie, my pet, you're not the type to enslave men, sweet though you are."

Lucie felt her cheeks go crimson but tossed her head.

"You wait and see. I'm going to change my ways."

"Good luck to you, duckie," said Maggie.

'*Good luck! I need it!*' thought Lucie.

Perhaps when she journeyed with her luggage to Keynwood on that May day which was to mark the beginning of her new life, she was for once over-confident. Certainly she felt no psychic stirrings to warn her of any pitfalls and troubles that might lie ahead.

She had left her niece and nephew rather unhappily, because they both wept and begged her not to go. But she had no compunction about Maggie. She had fallen on her feet and already found a nice German girl (with the stirring name of Brunhilda) to help her.

"I'll come home one Sunday and tell you all that's happening," Lucie said gaily, when she left Hove. They kissed, and Maggie made a frivolous remark about Lucie coming back with an engagement ring.

"I'll be tickled pink if you land your Mr. Randall," were her last words.

Lucie smiled as she remembered them, but it was no laughing matter really. This last fortnight of waiting to go to Keynwood and preparing her clothes had taught her how much Nat still meant to her.

Happy, optimistic, she arrived at the school, undaunted by the fact that it was an all-too typical first of May; a few degrees colder than it had been yesterday, and pouring with rain. The playing fields were sodden. The garden looked forlorn and the whole place had a dreary air.

This time she was admitted not by the daughter of the house, but by a fresh-faced Danish girl in a blue overall, who was one of the domestic staff. They were all back now. Mrs. Egbert, the English cook, Tom, the odd-job man, Betty and Ann, the dailies. Betty was a good fifty and had grey hair, but was one of the hard workers and mainstays of the place. Lucie grew to like her. She was an inveterate smoker and knowing that Mrs. Friern disliked the 'dailies' smoking, was always running into corners or locking herself in one of the lavatories in order to have a puff or two. She had a strong Cockney sense of humour and made Lucie laugh. Ann was nineteen and had long hair curling to her shoulders and only two passions in life—dancing and boy-friends.

Unlike that quiet morning when Lucie was interviewed by the Head, Keynwood today was buzzing with activity. The wheels had started to run, set in motion by Mr. and Mrs. Friern twenty-four hours before the parents turned up with their 'darlings.'

"Weeping day, termorrer, as I call it," Betty confided in Lucie. "The pore little things. Them youngest ones when they're 'omesick, they fair breaks my 'eart. As I says to my 'usband when I gets 'ome, I can't think 'ow the mums 'ave the 'eart to send 'em away from 'ome so young.''

With a fast developing sense of loyalty to the school which stiffened her pride on her first day there, Lucie felt bound to point out to Betty that school was necessary for little boys and that there was a lot to be said for the English system of boarding school even for the 'little weepers' aged seven.

They soon stopped weeping, as Lucie speedily learned. All was well once the parents departed. It was generally the fond and anxious mothers who caused the trouble. Once *they'd* gone, the boys settled down. And Lucie found out that they all loved the Headmaster. He commanded their immediate respect and confidence.

She found out, too, that they adored Geoffrey Mallow who was a sort of god to them because he had once played cricket for Sussex. What they felt about Nat Randall, Lucie wasn't sure for a long time. But she didn't imagine he'd be quite as popular as Mallow.

Today, Lucie met Mrs. Friern for the first time: a tall commanding woman with a slightly baleful eye that scared Lucie. Mrs. Friern was obviously going to be a strict disciplinarian. Her whole heart was in the school. She was 'Mrs. Keynwood'—and displayed the fact. Everything was for the school.

'*We do this at Keynwood*' or '*We don't do this*'. She praised and quoted and droned on endlessly about Lucie's duties and how she was to work, and why, and when.

"I trust you are a punctual person, Miss Reed," she said, with a rather grim smile which didn't exactly warm Lucie's heart, and told her always to go to her, Stella Friern, if Lucie was ever in any doubt about the boys' health or welfare generally. She would see Lucie later, she said, about the rest of her work.

One of Lucie's special cares would be the eight-year-old twins, Peter and Paul Graham. They were delicate and she must take their temperatures if she saw the slightest sign of fever. There was also a little new boy aged seven coming, named Jeremy Finch. Mrs Friern had seen the mother, Lady Finch, and decided that Jeremy had been hopelessly spoiled. One of those curly-headed darlings, who must be taught the way he should go.

"We are always kind, I hope, but we don't encourage molly-coddling," Mrs. Friern told her.

Lucie unpacked and put her room in some sort of order. Lunch was at one o'clock. She was told that she would hear a gong. Then, of course, she would meet the rest of the staff. *That meant Nat too.* She felt quite weak at the thought of seeing him. She was quite sure he wouldn't have heard she was coming here. How should he? He had been away.

Lucie looked out of the window and through the drenching rain could see the lissom figure of Barbie Friern hurrying through the grounds. She wore a green transparent mackintosh and hood. Lucie thought how smart she looked even in a mac, glanced at her own reflection and grimaced. In one of her new fresh white overalls, starched, as they used to be in hospital, she was not glamorous, she decided. But she had a colour today because she had spent the last fortnight in the sun on the front with the children. The slight tan suited her.

Suddenly, unaccountably vain, she took off her glasses and put them in her pocket as she went downstairs. She wanted to look her absolute *best* when she met *him* again.

In the long corridor, which she was forever afterwards to associate with the smell of rubber-flooring, polished woodwork, and the smell of cooking drifting from the kitchen—she ran into Geoffrey Mallow. He never walked. He strode, like a man on a deck, curly head slightly lowered as though against a wind. He almost crashed into her, muttering an apology; then said, "Oh, hullo there."

Then he moved on, but stopped and called back to her over his shoulder:

"Anything I can do for you–er–Matron?"

"No thank you," she answered, smiling at her new name, but had to admit she was glad he had asked, and that he was here at Keynwood.

Then suddenly she forgot Geoffrey Mallow completely, for she saw another man coming down the corridor with a brief-case in one hand. He did not see her but walked straight into the common-room.

It was Nat.

Nat just as she remembered him—so very good-looking—moving slowly and more gracefully than Mr. Mallow.

'Now,' thought Lucie, 'I must behave like Marta would do—*here goes*!' And she deliberately followed the History and

English master into the room. She gambled on the fact that she would find him alone, since the rest of the school was so busy; and she won. Only Nat was there. He stood rummaging in the brief-case which he had put out on a long oak table in the middle of the room, pulling out books and papers.

Lucie spoke his name breathlessly.

"Nat."

He glanced up. She could see the profound astonishment that widened his eyes. Then the Lucie who meant to be so confident vanished. It was a frightened girl who felt her knees knocking together who added:

"Surprised to see me?"

"That's putting it mildly. What on earth are *you* doing here?"

"I'm the new matron."

"*You?*"

"Yes."

They both stood still, staring at each other.

Whatever Nat Randall was thinking, Lucie felt an acute sense of discouragement because he neither smiled nor held out his hand. He seemed to freeze. And when he spoke it was in the coldest voice:

"I'm afraid I don't quite understand . . ." he began.

Lucie interrupted. She explained hurriedly, and not very happily now, how she had answered the advertisement and been given the job.

"I thought you were going to be a hospital nurse," said Nat Randall, staring at her.

Lucie glanced nervously at the door, terrified that somebody would come in at any moment.

"I'll have to explain later. I'm sure there isn't time now."

She watched him bite his lips, a habit she knew. It meant that he was ill-at-ease, even cross. Her heart was sinking lower and lower. For days and nights she had thought of this reunion, dreamed of it, imagined it would be the most glorious moment of her life. Bitterly disappointed by his reception of her she asked in a choking voice:

"Aren't you pleased to see me, Nat?"

He locked his brief-case, then looked at her again. His face seemed expressionless now. But the man's mind was teeming with thoughts of the past—as well as the present. It had come as a decided shock to him to see that *petite* figure in the white overall—to look again upon that shy, rather piquant face, once so familiar to him. To have Lucie back in his life, in the very school in which he worked, was something he could not accept casually—just as though they had met by mere chance. In a way, Nat Randall was angry—even shocked. (Shocked, too, by his own reactions.) He never had been able to look down into Lucie Reed's strangely pure, long-lashed eyes without recognising the beauty in them. A beauty and truth, perhaps, that he did not want thrust before him. He could not fail to see all the old trustful adoration in those eyes. In a way, of course, it flattered him. But he took refuge in sarcasm.

"I'm so pleased to see you, my dear, that I'm struck dumb."

His smile was cold. He came toward her but did not touch even her hand.

"I hope you'll be very happy here," he added, stiffly. "Not that I would envy any matron her job. But you'll cope, I'm sure. You were always efficient."

The praise stung rather than pleased Lucie. Her whole body was trembling and she found it difficult—almost impossible— to remain cool, to display indifference to him. She choked:

"Efficient—in what? I'd like to know!"

"We'll have an opportunity to talk together later on, I'm sure," he said. "I'm afraid I must go now. The Head expects me in his study."

His icy approach and the obvious dismay he had displayed when first he saw her froze Lucie as though she had suddenly crashed into sheer ice. Nat walked out of the room and left her alone, her face milk-white, her eyes enormous and panic-stricken.

She knew well that she was just as desperately in love with Nat Randall as ever. But she had a horrible feeling that he was angry because she had come. She felt defeated at the very start of this difficult love game which she had elected to play against a man who was a veritable expert at it.

She covered her face with her hands.

"Oh, I wish I hadn't come! I wish I hadn't come!"

She said the words aloud. Then she heard the sharp voice of Mrs. Friern calling down the corridor:

"Matron! Matron! I want you! *Where is Matron?* Has anybody seen the girl?"

4

FOR an instant Lucie felt so stupid with disappointment and
misery that she hardly responded to her new name. Then
the old Lucie reasserted herself. Pride waved a flag in the face
of threatened defeat. She lifted her chin. Her cheeks burned
red. She had taken this job here in Keynwood. Very well, she
was going to stay here and see it through; not crawl away
humiliated and afraid because Nat had given her such a poor
reception. She would show him that *she* was the strong one;
no longer the timid, adoring young girl of the past whom he
could just pick up and then throw down—at a whim.

She marched into the corridor and found Mrs. Friern,
carrying a wooden board in one hand and a bundle of papers
in the other. Her sour face bore a decidedly cross expression.

"Ah, there you are, Matron," she snapped as she saw Lucie.
"I've been trying to find you. This is our busiest day. I need
your help."

"Yes, Mrs. Friern," Lucie said meekly.

"Follow me into the First Form. We can be quiet there. I
want you to help me get this notice-board finished. I didn't
have time last night. I'm very behindhand, after having to be
away with my mother. So aggravating ... everything comes at
once ... so many new boys this term ... we'll have to put in
some extra time."

Lucie followed the tall, angular figure into Form I. She
looked with scant interest at the pleasant light room with its
pale-green painted walls which were hung with gay charts and
pictures, at the blackboard on which there was already the
coloured botanical drawing of a curiously naked-looking flower,
and at the rows of shiny varnished desks, waiting for the arrivals
tomorrow, for the new term to begin.

Mrs. Friern seated herself at the teacher's desk on the dais.
Lucie stood behind her and watched while Mrs. Friern
explained about the making of this time-table for the first-
formers.

The girl tried to listen attentively. Fixtures for showers and
bedtime, meals and health inspections, etc.—all items which
directly concerned the matron. Mrs. Friern finally left her to

write it all out in large print. The board must be ready to hang up later today. Lucie went to work and tried to feel really interested in her job.

But she kept thinking of Nat. He had spoiled everything. She could think of nothing but the dismay in his eyes and the coldness of the voice with which he had welcomed her. She felt devastated.

When she had finished her work she took the board to Mrs. Friern's room. It was all she could do to force herself to go into that room, because suddenly she heard Nat's voice and knew that *he* was in there. She found him, standing beside the woman, smoking a cigarette, smiling at the Head's wife with all the rather insolent charm that Lucie so well remembered. He was obviously no longer cross. He even smiled quite broadly at Lucie as she entered the room.

"I'm sorry you don't agree with me, Stella . . ." he said, addressing Mrs. Friern.

What had she said that he did not agree with? Lucie wondered. And he called her 'Stella'. He had been here so long, she must be an old friend of his now; and she was a *woman*. Nat was nice even to the most unattractive women. Mrs. Friern at her desk looked up at him with a warmth that transformed her sour, plain face. It was clear to Lucie that even the Headmaster's conventional wife found it easy to smile at Nat Randall. Then the two of them turned to the young girl in the white overall. Lucie, with admirable control, did not look in Nat's direction.

"I've finished this job, Mrs. Friern."

"Oh, thanks, Matron," said Stella Friern, resuming her rather fussy, authoritative manner. Then she added, "Meet Mr. Randall, our History and English master."

Now Lucie dared to look at Nat. But to her surprise and pleasure there was no coldness in his eyes this time. He gave her a slow, lazy, amused sort of smile and drawled:

"We've already met, haven't we, Matron?"

"Y . . . yes . . ." Lucie stammered.

"Oh, have you?" said Mrs. Friern vaguely. She had forgotten this. But she did not bother to enquire further into the matter. It did not really worry her as to when or where the two had met. She stood up, notice-board under her arm.

"We must get on. . ." she said, and sailed out of the room.

Lucie was to become accustomed to these words.

Stella Friern was always having to 'get on'.

Lucie turned and would have followed her, only suddenly Nat called her back.

"Lucie . . ." He said the name softly.

She turned and faced him, stiff as a ramrod.

"Yes, Mr. Randall ?"

Now he gave a low laugh.

"I say! That's pretty formal!"

"I'm sure it's the correct thing now that we both work at Keynwood," said Lucie. Her hands were trembling.

"Oh, very correct!" he said in a teasing voice.

She felt as she had so often done in the past—that he was mocking her. She wished she could hate him. But she was wildly excited in his presence and conscious of a warmth permeating her being; such a warmth as she had never felt with anybody else in the world.

"I just can't get over you becoming the matron here, my dear!" he observed.

She stared at him. She knew that he was a creature of moods but she really could not understand him. How was it that he could be so friendly now, when half an hour ago he had behaved as though she was the last person he had wanted to see ?

Her eyes flashed behind the glasses that could not quite conceal their brilliance. Nat Randall, looking down into them, thought how beautiful those eyes were. He had always wished little Lucie need not wear the horn-rims.

He had meant never to see her again. There was a child-like candour and innocence about Lucie Reed that had appealed to him strangely last summer and yet finally had driven him away from her. Adept though he was at dealing with that age-old attraction that can spark at a touch or a word between man and woman, he preferred to play the game with somebody who knew all the rules. He thought he had proved that Lucie was not in that class. He was not gratuitously cruel and did not want to hurt her. He had discovered that she was capable of being hurt in a way that the others in his life could never have been. So he had just dropped out. And now he had other ideas . . . other plans . . . with Barbara Friern so close at hand! After all, a master in Keynwood School would be in a strong position if he was 'well in with' the Head's daughter. It had definite advantages. Besides—Barbara was extremely attractive.

Nat had almost forgotten Lucie. Almost, but not quite. When he had seen her again here today and realised she had taken this job at Keynwood, he had been afraid that she had done so just in order to cast her feminine net about him again and the idea had annoyed him. But the annoyance had passed now—just as all emotions with Nat passed. Nothing lasted long with him. Now the old warmth that he used to feel for Lucie began to revive. His masculine vanity was touched by the sight of those big, rather reproachful eyes. He did not really want to be brutal with her, or any girl so young and gentle. He behaved more generously than he had done at first.

"Do forgive me for my discourtesy when we met in the common-room earlier on," he said suddenly, holding out a hand to her, "but you rather took me by surprise. I was in a hell of a rush, too. I'm terribly sorry. I'm really delighted to see you again, little *Santa Lucia.*"

The old pet name fell as pleasantly as music on her ears. She took his outstretched hand and all her misery fell away like a dark cloak as she felt the nervous strength of those fingers. She was left defenceless and once more open to the old fascination of this man.

"Perhaps I oughtn't to have come here . . ." she stammered, ". . . at least without telling you first, Nat, but I thought it would be such fun."

"I think it will be, too," he said frankly, "the others in the staff are not all that inspiring. It will be lots of fun to have you here, my dear."

She thrilled.

"Oh Nat, do you mean it?"

"Of course."

"I'm sure I oughtn't to stay and talk to you here. I ought to go . . ." she began, breathlessly.

He thought how charming she was; he had always thought that, and once more he was sincere when he said:

"Don't go. Stay and tell me just a bit about everything. Mrs. F. won't mind. I'm not forbidden to talk to the matron, anyhow."

As he questioned her about herself and her reasons for taking this job, she gathered courage and remained with him. She told him about the changes that fate had brought about in her life. How after leaving the hospital in order to look after Maggie and the children she had felt disinclined to take up nursing again because she had been out of it so long. And what a temptation it had been to apply for this post when she saw it advertised.

Even now, she wondered if Nat was taking in all that she said. Those dark, thickly-lashed eyes of his were flickering here, there, everywhere, so restlessly, and he was lighting another cigarette from the stub of the one he had just finished. He had always been a chain-smoker, she thought, with a pang at her heart.

"I'm sure I ought to go," she said again in an agony of sudden shyness and fear that the Headmaster, himself, might come in and think it odd that she should be in Mrs. Friern's room alone with the History master.

"See you at lunch, then," murmured Nat, "and I'd like to have a longer talk, because there's a lot I want to tell you about myself. I always used to find it soothing to talk to you and hear your opinions, Lucie. We obviously can't display our old friendship to the whole school, but we can meet sometimes. I'll find a way of seeing you. Look—I'll leave a note in your letter-box. Our mail goes into those pigeon-holes in the hall."

"I'll look for it," she said, her heart leaping.

"I'll write something marvellous," he joked.

"You were always thoroughly conceited," she said and laughed, biting her lip.

"I don't believe you like me any more," he said sadly. "And you've been playing such a heroic part at home. I'm not surprised. I named you rightly, little Saint Lucie, didn't I?"

"Well, I'm *not* a saint," Lucie said rather angrily, "and you know I don't like being called one."

"I'll reserve my own opinion," he smiled.

"How like old times," Lucie said. "How often I've heard you say that, Nat, and how about me reserving *my* opinion for a change?"

"About me?"

That streak of vanity—the desire to dominate and enslave —crept over the man as he stood there looking down at this small, sweet girl whom he realised, with some surprise, he had missed. She had become more necessary to him than he had imagined. Maybe because she fed his vanity. Maybe because he found her so much more adorable, (and less trouble) than Barbie Friern—and other girls like Barbie—who needed constant flattering, or maybe because there was an intangible *something* between himself and Lucie Reed which drew them irresistibly toward each other. Only for Nat emotion meant a lightning flash—blazing, then vanishing until the next moment of storm. But for Lucie it was a long-drawn-out ecstasy. He knew that. He was filled in this ungovernable moment with the longing to reassert his mastery of her emotions.

"Don't hate me, Lucie," he said in a low voice, "and don't let us say good-bye to each other—ever again."

The blood rose to her face. She stared at him stupefied. "Do you mean that . . . ?" she whispered.

He took her hands and drew her close but only for an instant. Then he kissed both the hands—a swift caress on each palm which left her speechless with joy. Maggie's warnings, Marta's philosophies about letting a man think himself a conqueror, vanished. Almost she had been in his arms; felt his breath against her cheek.

Then he let her go again. He spoke casually:

"Darling Lucie, you were so nice to me all last year—let me try and help you here where this life in a boys' school may be tough for you until you get used to it. I must go now, but I'll see you soon."

When Lucie went back to the common-room just before lunch, her heart was singing.

She found Geoffrey Mallow there talking to a short woman with dark, close-cropped hair, which was turning grey. She had young-looking blue eyes and a fresh complexion, but her appearance was spoilt by a bad figure and rather big teeth. She was introduced to Lucie as Miss Day. Lucie was soon to learn that the boys called poor Beryl Day 'Horsey' because of those big teeth. She came in for a lot of mockery and took it well. She rushed at Lucie, and with a friendly grin said:

"Oh, I *am* pleased to meet you, Miss Reed. It's splendid for us to have such a nice young matron—isn't it, Geoffrey?" She turned to Mr. Mallow.

Lucie rather thought that Geoffrey gave her an odd grin behind Beryl's back but couldn't be sure. Anyhow, he said:

"Jolly nice."

Miss Day seized Lucie by the arm.

"I expect you're feeling very lost on your first day. I'll show you round and tell you everything after lunch. You must call me Berry; they all do."

"Thank you very much, Berry," Lucie said.

Another girl came into the room—tall and thin—and was introduced to Lucie as Joanna Parrish. She was a non-resident mistress who taught Music and Singing. She had come today, so Beryl whispered to Lucie, to arrange her curriculum for the term.

"Isn't it nice?" Miss Day then gushed to Joanna Parrish, "to have such a young matron. When Mrs. Friern originally told us another elderly one was coming, I was fed up. Glad she never materialised!"

Geoffrey put his pipe into his pocket and walked out, murmuring the word 'lunch'.

"Let's go, I'm famished," said Miss Day, and followed him.

For a moment Lucie was left alone with the Music mistress, who returned Lucie's gaze gravely. Lucie could see that she was a reserved sort of girl. It would not be easy to get to know Joanna Parrish. Later, Berry told Lucie that Joanna had once intended to be a concert pianist, but her family had lost their money and she had had to take this job of teaching little school-boys. Lucie could imagine what torture it must be to a fine musician to hear them thumping and playing wrong notes all day when her soul yearned for good music. But she never complained.

She looked at Lucie in her gentle way and said:

"You'll find the staff easy to get on with. I'm sure you'll like it here."

"I'm sure I will," Lucie nodded.

"Sometimes I wish I was a resident. One has divided loyalties when one lives out, and always has to hurry home," said Joanna. "If you live *in* the school you can give your heart to it."

"Why don't you live here, then?"

"My father is totally incapacitated by arthritis and my mother and I have to lift him between us. She couldn't do without me."

As Lucie walked with Joanna down the corridor to the dining-room, she was filled with desire to mention the all-important name of Nat Randall to Miss Parrish.

She had already met Mr. Randall, she told Joanna.

Lucie thought she saw a strange, secretive look enter Joanna Parrish's fine grey eyes. She could also sense her complete withdrawal, for she said coldly:

"Oh, really? He's a very clever man, isn't he?"

At once Lucie was left to wonder if Nat had used some of
that remorseless charm of his upon this quiet, rather noble girl
who so patiently taught music to unmusical children, or encouraged those with talent. Lucie was alive with curiosity and
interest in everything and everybody, as she sat down to lunch
which they had today in the Headmaster's private dining-room,
as they were such a small number. Miss Day, who sat next to
Lucie had constituted herself chief informant, and told Lucie
that they would be lunching in the big dining-room with the
boys tomorrow.

But it was hard for Lucie to think of anything but that
delirious moment when Nat had kissed those two hands which
she had folded in her lap now, and was twisting nervously
together.

5

THE Headmaster and his wife took their places at the table.
Geoffrey sat on Mrs. Friern's right, Nat on her left. He
was at the other end of the table from Lucie.

Barbara Friern came in a moment later and seated herself on
the other side of Nat. Try as Lucie would, not to look at him,
her gaze was continually drawn to his face. Once or twice he
glanced at her and gave a little smile and nod. But he did not
address her. Barbara kept him well occupied. What a change
in her when she was in Nat's company, Lucie thought. There
was nothing languid or bored about her demeanour now. She
was sparkling. She talked more than anybody else—obviously
used to monopolising the conversation, anxious to be *the*
personality of the group.

She was often quite witty in a rather malicious way. And
Nat laughed with and at her. Lucie could see how attentive he
was, passing her the condiments, picking up her table-napkin
when she dropped it, being the cavalier, charming Nat, whom
Lucie knew so well.

The Head talked almost continually to Geoffrey. He was
interested in some account of a nature school Mr. Mallow had
just visited in the Italian mountains. Miss Day chatted to
Lucie, who tried to give her her full attention, but found her,
as everybody seemed to do, a little trying. Joanna Parrish sat

silent, always silent as Lucie soon got to know, lost in her own sad thoughts and vanished dreams.

Herta, the Danish girl, served the meal. It was not bad. A roast, followed by rhubarb pie and cheese. Funny, Lucie thought, but she knew that Nat would refuse the rhubarb. She remembered that he didn't like puddings, also that he was a bit of a *gourmet*. One of the crosses he had to bear in school life, he once told her, was having to put up with a monotonous, and often stodgy, diet. But Geoffrey Mallow took two helpings of the pie and obviously enjoyed his food in a healthy school-boyish fashion.

He had become lost in his graphic description of the students he met in Cortina bronzing their young bodies in the sun and the snow, and how they came down from the mountain heights to search for the lovely flowers in the valleys. He mentioned a few Latin names which only the Head seemed to understand. He was interested in Mr. Mallow's botany.

"It's amazing," Geoffrey said, his rather fine eyes turned to the Head, "how the gentian root produces twelve to fifteen per cent sugar. Uncrystallisable, of course, but they use it for making this fantastic cordial spirit."

"Ah, yes," nodded Mr. Friern. "It has an unpronounceable name, hasn't it?"

Miss Day gave a hearty laugh.

"I'm sure Mr. Mallow could pronounce it. He adores his terrible tongue-twisters."

Geoffrey's eyes twinkled at her.

"Yes, Miss Day, it is *enzianbranntwein*."

"Oh, don't!" screamed Miss Day.

Barbara Friern now turned her attention from Nat to the Languages master.

"Sounds like a character from one of those frightful German operas."

Here, suddenly, Joanna Parrish made one of her rare entrances into the discussion.

"Do you really think German opera is so frightful, Miss Friern?"

Miss Friern drawled:

"I can't say I have much use for *The Ring* or any of those horrid long-drawn-out epics about Valhalla and the rest."

"I find Wagner opera both beautiful and stimulating," said Joanna gravely.

"Each man to his taste," said Barbara, reverting to her languid voice now that she was speaking to one of her own sex.

Lucie, after listening quietly to this discussion, decided to back Miss Parrish.

"I've only been once to Covent Garden and that was to hear *Tristan and Isolde*. I thought it was absolutely wonderful."

Miss Friern shot what Lucie thought rather a withering look at her but said nothing. Nat caught Lucie's eye and put in his spoke.

"All that heavy Teutonic sentimentality leaves me cold, I am afraid, and I really can't abide those colossal *prima donnas* who try to cover their bulk with Siegfried's shield. It's apt to tickle my sense of humour, and one oughtn't to display humour at a Wagner opera, ought one?"

Everybody except Miss Parrish laughed. Lucie saw Nat smiling, glancing now at the perfect profile of the Headmaster's daughter.

"It's a pity *you* don't warble, Barbie," he said. "You'd have made such a splendid Isolde. But they never look like you." Then he added to Miss Parrish: "You'll admit that, Joanna?"

But Miss Parrish was not to be drawn into further talk and stared down at her plate in stony silence. Barbie looked through her lashes at Nat.

"I can't see myself as an Isolde," she said. "I don't sing, and I would never dream of thrusting a knife in my breast out of grief for any man."

Lucie could well believe that. Nat laughed, as though what she said appealed to his sense of humour. Lucie began to wonder what he really felt about the beautiful red-head.

Now Geoffrey Mallow spoke. Lucie could see that he hadn't really been paying any attention to the conversation and was still thinking about his gentian.

"Strange to think," he said, "that from that modest little flower such a deadly poison can be distilled."

"Beautiful things are so often poisonous," put in Beryl Day, with her toothy smile.

Lucie dared not look at Barbara now, but as the girl rose from the table and Nat with her, Lucie thought she saw their hands touch. It might have been purely accidental. She wasn't to know. But for the second time that day hope and joy crashed down into a dust of doubt and jealousy.

She remained in her place and thought that she was there

alone, but suddenly heard Geoffrey Mallow's deep, nice voice behind her. She turned and found him lighting a pipe. As she looked up, he eyed her though the smoke.

"Coming in to coffee, Matron? It's the one luxury we, on the staff, are allowed twice daily. I do like coffee after my meals, don't you?"

Lucie tried to turn her attention to him, her heart warmed by his friendliness. Blunt, he might be, but he was a discerning man and he must have felt that she was a little like a fish out of water, and so had come back to encourage her. She followed him into the common-room feeling only too well aware that she *was* a 'fish' swimming right out of her depth, oblivious of the dangerous rapids that might await her.

"Later on you must let me take you round the garden," Geoffrey suggested. "There's one little bit of ground which the Head has given me, in which I raise a few special plants. I like experimenting. Would it interest you to see the results?"

Lucie told him that she didn't know anything about gardening but that she would be very interested and would like to see the flowers with him. She felt that he was trying to be especially nice because it was her first day here.

She watched him strike another match. He had big strong hands in keeping with his tall athletic frame—hands that could bowl a cricket ball with tremendous energy and aim, and yet, she supposed, handle a tiny fragile flower with the utmost delicacy. She thought of Nat's slim fingers and well-kept nails. They could be gentle, and yet they could hurt. Those fingers had touched Barbie's just now. *Was he having an affair with the Headmaster's daughter?* Had she, Lucie, come blundering into this school only to have her heart battered and bruised all over again?

"Be seeing you," said Geoffrey, and sauntered out of the common-room leaving Lucie with the rest of the staff, lost in her unenviable reflections.

She had plenty to do, settling down to her new job, however. She was soon to grow familiar with the big laundry room full of linen baskets and cupboards, and a long table at which she was to spend many hours mending the boys' clothes, and checking and sorting laundry, making lists with Herta or, at times, working with Mrs. Friern herself. She was shown the locked cupboard behind which lay the medicines, and given the key of it as her sacred charge. She visited all the bedrooms and listened to Mrs. Friern while she told her which boy slept in which bed, and what the procedure was for supervising the youngest ones at their baths, getting them to bed—and the rest of it.

The Head, himself, Mrs. Friern said, made a habit of going around every night to say good-night to all the boys after which Lucie must turn out the lights.

Lucie gravely announced that she would do her best.

She did not see Nat again until after supper time. She was far too busy and so was he, making his own preparations for the morrow.

All during that busy afternoon she found herself irresistibly drawn toward the front hall—to glance in that pigeon-hole marked 'R' in which Nat had told her she would find her letters. *In which he had told her he would slip a note.*

When would he put it there? What would he write? Presumably it would be just to tell her at what time he could meet her and where. Perhaps it would be somewhere in the school-house. Perhaps out-of-doors, far away from the buildings, where they wouldn't be seen.

Lucie alternated between a deliciously wicked pleasure at the thought of a clandestine meeting with Nat . . . and the sickening fear that he might have said that he would leave that note for her, but would never do so.

She must have faith, she told herself a dozen times. She must believe now that he was glad she had come to Keynwood. After all, this was only the first day here. It wasn't reasonable of her to suppose that Nat would find time for a meeting *today*.

But what a long time away tomorrow seemed—and still further the next day and the next.

Lucie was hopelessly in love again. She meekly acknowledged the fact to herself. And she was sure it was going to be both heaven and hell living at Keynwood under the same roof as Nat.

At last she exercised her will-power and went no more into the front hall to examine those pigeon-holes. Anyhow, hers was always empty, she told herself with pessimism. The last post had brought but few letters and there was nothing for Miss Reed.

At supper time, she was quite worn-out with physical and mental stress. Soon after seven she had finished doing all the jobs that Mrs. Friern had allocated to her. She took off the white overall and put on a blue linen dress—the sort of thing

Miss Day had suggested they wore for the evening meal in the summer. Lucie began to look forward to seeing Nat in the dining-room. But fresh disappointment was in store for her. There were only two people at supper, Mr. Mallow and Miss Day. The talkative Berry provided the information for which Lucie dared not ask.

"Nat Randall is out for supper tonight."

Lucie sat with her hands tightly clenched in her lap. She was so bitterly disappointed at not seeing Nat that it was absurd, she thought. She tried to speak lightly:

"Where are the Frierns?"

"The Head's got a brother in Horsham—a lawyer," said Berry, "they always go over there to dinner the night before term starts."

"And Miss Friern, too?"

But it was Geoffrey, helping himself to the potatoes that Herta had just put on the table, who unconsciously delivered the real blow.

"No, she's out with our Mr. Randall who is playing chauffeur to her. I met him about half an hour ago getting out his car when I was putting mine away. Barbie had a date of some kind in Brighton. He told me she had asked him to drive her in." Then . . . "Have some potato, Matron?" It was Geoffrey speaking to Lucie. She automatically took hold of the spoon and helped herself from the vegetable dish. She had lost all appetite. Her heart had sunk to the very depths.

She wouldn't be seeing Nat tonight, and there wouldn't be any note in her letter-box. He was, now, at this very moment, driving Barbara Friern into Brighton.

6

LUCIE that following day had no time in which to think of herself and Nat. It was the beginning of term. There were about forty boys at Keynwood. From early afternoon onward they began to arrive in the company of their fond parents. One small boy arrived in the smartest Rolls Lucie had ever seen. She was never to forget her first meeting with the Finch family. They were almost the last to appear.

It was a mild day. The sun had already mopped up the damp of last night's rain. The playing fields looked fresh and green. The swimming-pool sparkled and the flower-beds were a blaze of tulips. The house was garnished and some of the classrooms had had a new coat of paint.

Lucie, putting aside personal worries completely, watched with interest as the pupils arrived. The majority appeared to her unperturbed, their cheeks bulging with sweets, as they hailed their pals and went into huddles to chatter and giggle and exchange reminiscences of the Easter 'hols'. She could hardly hear herself speak with all the chattering voices. But she was quick to see that one or two of the smaller boys stood near their mothers, obviously trying to be manly but clinging on, tight-lipped, dewy-eyed, besieged by the awful pangs of the coming separation. Lucie was so sorry for *them*. And her heart was really touched when she first saw Jeremy Finch walking between his mother and father, carrying a very small new attaché case. Everything about him was new.

The uniform—dark green blazer, grey flannels, white shirt and Keynwood tie which was green with a pink stripe—it all looked too big for him. He was somewhat undersized for his seven years. He twisted his cap nervously in one hand. Lucie imagined he had once had curls, but the fair hair had been given a crew cut. His eyes looked enormous, blue and full of panic, flicking from side to side as he walked. *Panic* was the word. Poor mite, Lucie thought; why send a child so young to boarding school? If he had been hers, she could not have borne to part with him or cause this agony, but she heard, afterwards, that it had been a question of getting him into the school this term or not at all, as they were so booked up at Keynwood. She was also to learn that the parents, Sir Mark and Lady Finch, were about to separate and that this was their last visit to the school together.

During that next few weeks at Keynwood Hall, Lucie was to learn about many things, and particularly the evils of divorce and how deeply it affected children. All the little Finch boy's sufferings arose from the egotism and selfishness of his parents.

Sir Mark looked to Lucie rather a nice man, although he had a somewhat weak face. But he had charming manners and was obviously fond of the boy and anxious for him to get on.

The person Lucie took a dislike to was Lady Finch. She was

a self-centred, rather silly woman, Lucie thought. In her early thirties, it was from her that Jeremy had inherited the big blue eyes and the blond hair. She was glamorous. Her big green droopy straw hat was very fashionable—like her short linen suit. She wore pointed green shoes with high stiletto heels. She had one of those child-like voices which Lucie found annoying. Mr. Friern, himself, was walking beside the Finches. He stopped when he saw Lucie and introduced them.

"Our matron, Miss Reed, who will look after your boy. Matron—Sir Mark and Lady Finch."

Sir Mark greeted Lucie with a formal bow and a tired smile.

"How d'you do. Hope our little rascal won't give too much trouble. But I've tried to teach him to be fairly civilised."

Here Anthea Finch put an arm around the shrinking boy and exclaimed:

"He behaves *divinely*. You'll find him *adorable*, Matron, and I'm absolutely *wretched* having to part with him, but I'm flying to the States tomorrow and we think it's just the best thing to do, to leave him here. Don't you agree, Matron?"

Lucie was taken aback. She did not really think it was the best thing, although she afterwards changed her mind when she heard what Lady Finch was like. She understood, then, why Mark Finch wanted to get his son away from that sugary maternal influence which would undermine any small boy's character. Lucie said:

"I'm sure he'll be happy here, Lady Finch, and I promise to keep a special eye on him."

"Now Jerry, angel," Anthea wheedled the boy, "see what a nice young matron you've got. I'm *sure* she'll give you a big cuddle every night, instead of me."

Lucie caught the Head's gaze. He looked quickly away. Lucie could sense that he was not amused. Jeremy's father put in quickly:

"I don't think Jeremy needs cuddling as much as a little of the hardening-up process, my dear Anthea. He's had too much cuddling and coddling already."

She gave him a dark look; obviously she didn't like him and didn't mind showing the fact. She even began to argue with him in front of total strangers like the Head and Lucie, and to say how hard he always was on 'poor little Jerry'. Sir Mark ended with the curt comment that young Jeremy's upbringing would now be left in the hands of Mr. Friern, and that he,

himself, would be down to see his son in a month's time. Here
Anthea Finch squealed:

"My poor poppet—all that long time wizzout seeing his
Mummy or Daddy."

'Idiot,' Lucie thought, for the little boy's face crumpled,
and now he burst into the tears which he could no longer
control.

Mr. Friern cast his eyes heavenwards. Lucie was sure he
must be thankful there were not many mothers like Lady Finch.
Most of them, these days, seemed sensible. They helped to
make the partings easy. Lucie decided that it would not be out
of place for her to intervene, so she took Jeremy's hand and
pulled him gently away from his mother.

"Would you like to come and see our aquarium, Jeremy?
Mr. Friern has a marvellous tank full of rare fish. It's about
feeding time, so, if you like, you could help me give them a
pinch of food. Then we'll go and inspect your bedroom and
you can meet the two boys who are going to sleep on either
side of you."

The wretched little boy tried to check his sobs. Lady Finch
dabbed at her eyes and looked sullenly at her husband who
muttered: "Thanks awfully," to Lucie.

Lucie led Jeremy away, talking to him as she used to do to
her nephew, Tim, who was exactly the same age, and a bit of
a cry-baby. She longed to sympathise but kept firmly off the
subject of the parting and in a few moments Jeremy dried his
tears and examined the tiny, darting, multi-coloured fish in
the big tank that stood in a recess leading off the main hall. It
was illuminated, and one of Mr. Friern's artistic triumphs.

Lucie could not stay too long with the little new boy because
there were others to look after. The Graham twins had come
and had to be taken care of. *They* were very different—delicate
in health they might be, thin and sallow, but hard little nuts
full of mischief. In no way did they seem distressed by the
farewell to their parents. Major and Mrs. Graham were a nice
sensible pair. He was in the Army and tomorrow they were both
flying out to Germany where the Major was stationed. The
twins were to join them there for the summer holidays.

Mrs. Graham confided in Lucie.

"You may find Peter and Paul a bit of a handful but they're
darlings, and they love it here. We're so delighted with Keynwood. To tell you the truth . . ." she brought her voice down

to a whisper . . . "I'm glad you've come, Miss Reed, as we weren't all that keen on the last matron. I thought she was a bit of a nagger, and rather sour. The twins didn't like her. But I can see they're going to like *you*."

That made Lucie feel good and quite important. She began to warm to her first day of term.

She managed to get the twins off on a tour of inspection with Jeremy Finch whom they promised to look after between them. She was quite glad to see the Finches drive away in their Rolls—and later when she saw the Grahams off in their somewhat battered Morris, she thought how much better it must be to be hard up and happy than wealthy and ill-matched. Mark Finch had obviously married the wrong girl, and poor little Jeremy was the unhappy product.

Lucie found it a little confusing at first meeting so many parents and listening to so many confidences from the anxious mothers.

"*Do see that Bill goes to bed early as he gets so terribly tired. He's outgrowing his strength.*"

"*Johnny simply must have his pills—here they are—at least once a week, as he needs them.*"

(Hastily Lucie marked John's name on the box of tablets.)

"*I'm afraid Martin has a sniffle but I don't think it's anything catching or I wouldn't have brought him back, but you might take his temperature tonight, Matron.*"

"*We're terribly sorry, Matron, we forgot young Oliver's third pair of pyjamas, but I'll be sending them on.*"

Orders, apologies, and some complaints.

One small boy had been miserable last term because the boy in the next bed was a bully and would she see that he changed his room. He was happy *really* but just didn't like *that* boy. Another mother didn't think her pet ought to be made to swim as he was terrified of water. The next said that she thought last term's food had been too starchy and her son was putting on too much weight. The next congratulated Keynwood on its wonderful food. One boy was a 'sleep-walker' and must be safeguarded. And so on . . .

Everybody was nice to Lucie personally. One or two of the fathers gave her a merry sidelong glance and teased her. They'd always thought that matrons should be motherly old souls, they said, and what was *she* doing in the school, looking, herself, a schoolgirl? (the usual form, thought Lucie, when people first saw her).

But it was all amusing and interesting and by supper time she felt as though she had suddenly become very old indeed, like the woman who lived in the shoe; she had so many children she really *didn't* know what to do. She was lucky enough to have a good memory and remembered most of the little boys' names and habits and did not get confused over the medicines or special requests.

Once or twice during the great upheaval of the afternoon she caught a glimpse of Nat. In well pressed grey flannels he looked handsome and debonair. He was busy talking to the various parents, but he never actually came Lucie's way until they all met for supper.

By this time, Keynwood Hall was comparatively quiet again. The boys had gone to bed. Lucie felt tired now. There had been so much rushing round up and down the stairs, as well as all the unpacking. Already she knew who was going to be her friend and who was going to *try* to antagonise her. There was one boy of twelve, named Brian Olifant, who was what she imagined to be a regular little 'tough guy'. He was well built, with a thick mop of dark hair and heavily marked brows, and not bad looking. Apparently he had excelled at games last term and was the champion swimmer last summer. But he soon showed Lucie that he was a conceited child and a boaster. He knew everything. He also hated discipline and was rude to Lucie when he was told to go to bed.

"I don't need a matron bossing me around. I'm a senior," he said and looked at the others in his room, waiting for the applause which they gave only half-heartedly. He was not popular. Lucie was firm with young Olifant and told him that she was here to look after him as well as the juniors, and that he'd better look smart and go to bed and stop 'sky-larking'. As she turned away, she caught the grimace he made at her. Yes, she would have trouble with Master Brian, she was sure. There was always one Terror in every school. This boy had obviously had too much television in the holidays and seen more films of shooting and violence than were good for him.

Lucy discovered that Geoffrey Mallow was good with boys of Brian's calibre. 'Get 'em out on the playing fields and teach them to kick a ball around or use a cricket bat in the proper manner'—that was his diet for little boys like Brian, and it worked.

For the most part she found the Keynwood boys delightful.

One or two obviously suffered from the pangs of homesickness and had to be jollied along and cheered up. But it was Jeremy Finch who wrung Lucie's heart.

She found him that night with his head under the bedclothes, trying to stifle an agony of weeping. She sat on the edge of the bed and whispered a few comforting words trying not to be too soft for his own sake. The twins were giggling together on the opposite side of the room. The small boy on Jeremy's right was already asleep. The one on his left sat up with arms around his hunched knees devouring one of the few comics which Mr. Friern thought healthy and allowed in the school.

He was a freckled, snub-nosed boy with an engaging smile. He grinned at Lucie. She remembered that his name was Iain Roberts.

"Hullo," he said.

"Hullo," she smiled back. *This* one was obviously not the homesick type. "How are you doing?"

"I like being at school," he said and pulled a piece of chewing gum from his mouth and drew it out until it snapped. He then held it up for inspection. "I've been chewing this for two days," he added proudly. "I put it on the table by my bed at home last night. Mum didn't see it."

Lucie shuddered and grimaced.

"Do you intend to stick it anywhere tonight?"

"Is it forbidden?" he asked, popping the horrible piece of gum back in his mouth.

"I don't think there is a hard and fast rule about it but it's a bit disgusting." She was still smiling. "Think of the germs you swallow."

"You don't swallow gum," said young Roberts promptly.

"But what about the germs?"

"My Dad's a doctor and he knows how to kill germs," boasted Roberts, "so I'm not scared."

Lucie repressed a laugh and contented herself with a warning to this bright and uninhibited young man.

"Just don't let me find it sticking to any of the furniture in this room, Roberts, or a black mark for you."

Roberts, chewing noisily and with a broad grin, pointed at Jeremy who was still weeping.

"Isn't he a cry-baby?"

"Now you settle down and put that comic away and remember that some boys don't find it so easy to be gay on their first night of term," said Lucie more severely. How hard-hearted little boys could be! She sat on the edge of Jeremy Finch's bed and touched his curly tousled head.

"Stop crying and let's have a chat, Finch," she said in a soft friendly voice.

"I want–to–go home," Jeremy stammered wildly.

Lucie begged him to take a grip of himself and remember that all the other boys had had to get used to school life and that he, too, would soon get to like it. Tomorrow when the lessons and games started he would find it all great fun.

Jeremy, however, was hysterical and not to be consoled. Then the Head, on his final rounds, appeared and took over from Lucie. She discovered now how good he was with the boys at a time like this. The panic in Jeremy Finch's eyes soon gave place to a smile. Mr. Friern made no allusions to the homesickness but began to tell the child a story about a golden cock-pheasant that had been found by Mr. Mallow with an injured wing, and how Mr. Mallow had built an aviary for it down at the bottom of the garden. Later, he said, one of the parents had given them a hen and they were hoping it would lay and that they would have young pheasants. It was amazing how that wing had healed, Mr. Friern said. Mr. Mallow was so clever with birds and flowers. Jeremy must see the golden pheasant tomorrow.

Jeremy was now interested. He asked several questions about the wounded bird. Bit by bit, he gained confidence. Finally he agreed to settle down and sleep. The Head, himself, promised to take him down to the aviary tomorrow morning.

Lights were turned out. In the corridor Mr. Friern whispered to Lucie.

"He'll get over it. Poor little blighter. Not much of a home life to stiffen the upper lip. Thoroughly coddled."

"I'll look in again in an hour, sir, and make sure he is all right," said Lucie.

"Thanks, Matron," he said, and added: "I hear you've been coping very nicely. They are a turbulent tribe when they first arrive but they soon calm down, you know."

Lucie felt gratified by this praise. She was thankful, anyhow, that she had not made a complete fool of herself at the very start of her job.

But at the table during the evening meal, back came the old

inferiority complex and the emotional disturbance that she had not had time to feel all day.

When would Nat Randall arrange to see her alone? She could not concentrate on the gossiping, chattering Miss Day. She found it excessively hard not to keep looking in Nat Randall's direction. But all the time she could hear that wonderful rich voice of his. He spoke beautiful English. In his capacity as master of literature he could quote the classics endlessly—both poetry and prose. He and Mrs. Friern were now discussing a poem written during the holidays by the head boy, Christopher Wynters.

"Wynters gave it to me when he arrived and I really must say I'm staggered," Nat remarked. "It's quite a remarkable sonnet. His father was telling me that the boy spends too much time reading and writing, but there you are—it's always the wrong parents who seem to have the wrong sons. Wynters was a rowing blue and wants his youngster to be a sportsman—but the lad is definitely a writer of the future. I warned Mr. Wynters that it was no good trying to quench the fires of genius."

"My husband and I were both saying what a remarkable boy Wynters is," put in Stella Friern. "The school's very lucky to have him. After all, he won a scholarship for Shrewsbury last term. His father ought to be proud of him."

"A pity he can't appreciate the sonnet," said Nat.

"Let's have a look at it," put in the Head.

Young Wynters' effort was passed round the table, and accorded much praise. It came to Lucie. She did not know a lot about classical poetry but she could see why Nat called Christopher Wynters 'a genius'. The sonnet was beautifully written—on the subject of Easter. Keynwood would obviously be losing a boy with a touch of greatness.

She handed the poem across the table back to Nat. As he took it, his gaze met hers. She felt that awful wild surge of the heart. It was uncontrollable even though she managed to mask her features. He smiled at her, impersonally, she thought.

"Well," he said, "how did it strike you, Matron?"

"I think it's a wonderful effort for a boy of thirteen," she answered, trying to speak as lightly as he did. "It might have been written by . . . by . . ."

"By whom, would you say?" cut in Barbara Friern suddenly. Lucie wondered if Miss Friern were trying to make her

look stupid and groped in her mind for the right name to
say, trying hard to remember her poets. Then she blurted
out:

"Oh, Shelley or Keats."

"Oh, I would never have said that," drawled Barbara.

But Nat suddenly said:

"I'm not sure Miss Reed isn't right. It *has* a quality of Percy
Bysshe."

Lucie's heart leapt again. She was absurdly pleased because
he had defended her analysis. She saw Barbara shrug her
shoulders and toss back a lock of red hair with one languid
hand. Mrs. Friern started to talk about the six o'clock radio
forecast which was fine weather for tomorrow. Geoffrey
Mallow spoke to Lucie.

"First day of cricket, Matron, so it had better be fine. Great
day for me."

The Head rose. Supper was ended.

7

Now, Lucie thought, now she really *must* talk to Nat, or go
crazy.

She caught his eye and felt that unconsciously she must
have sent out a burning, even entreating, look, because he
responded, narrowing his lids as he smiled at her, which was a
caress in itself. Brushing past her, through the doorway, he
whispered:

"*Postbag.*"

Lucie's whole body seemed to flame into life. She knew
what *that* meant. He must have written her a note just before
he came in to dinner. Her hungry heart beat so fast that she
hardly knew how to stop herself from rushing now, pell-mell
down the big empty corridor toward the main hall. Everything
seemed worse because Geoffrey unconscious of the fact that he
was doing the wrong thing, called to her:

"I say, Matron—care to wander out with me and have a look
at my aviary, after coffee?"

Lucie turned to him. She tried to look natural and speak
calmly.

"Terribly nice of you, but I . . . I've got some letters to write," she blurted.

He gave her his friendly smile in return and assured her that it didn't matter and that he'd take her to see the birds another time.

"Coming along for coffee?" Beryl Day's voice now detained Lucie.

She felt like a horse that was being reined in—straining against the bit—but once again she paused.

"Just a sec . . ." she answered like an excited schoolgirl, and fled down the passage toward the hall. Beryl Day looked after the *petite* figure and said to Geoffrey as they walked into the common-room:

"That's a nice kid."

"I like her," was Geoffrey's brief response, "I like her very much. I should think she's a very sensible sort of girl."

"Attractive, too," said Berry generously.

To that Mr. Mallow made no reply. It was so long since he had allowed himself to wonder whether a girl was 'attractive' or not. These last few years as a schoolmaster, he had thrown himself completely into his work. He was half inclined to believe that schoolmasters should remain bachelors and so be able to devote themselves to the boys and their careful upbringing. On the other hand he had to grant that the new little matron was what he would call an 'appealing' type. Shy. Not glamorous . . . but better . . . yes . . . a 'nice kid', as Berry declared.

Meanwhile the 'nice kid' who was supposed to be so sensible, was behaving in what she, herself, knew was a far from sensible fashion. She gave one brief ecstatic look at the pigeon-hole marked 'R'. Yes . . . *there* was the white envelope for which she had been waiting all day—all last evening, too. She seized it and tore it open. It was not the first note she had received from Nat Randall. She knew that small scholarly writing with the Greek 'e' which he favoured. It consisted of only one line and was unsigned. But it was quite enough to send her into the seventh heaven.

'Swimming pool, nine p.m.'

For safety's sake, she thought, she had better tear that note to shreds, but even as she did so she regretted having to part with it.

'*Oh, I love him, I love him. I'm mad about him. I always was and I always will be,*' she thought, dizzily.

Swimming pool, nine p.m. How funny that sounded really.

The swimming pool in a boys' prep school couldn't be a romantic place, she thought. Or could it? Well, tonight it assumed a mysteriously beautiful, romantic quality for Lucie. This assignation meant so much more to her than anyone could guess. It meant that Nat had not really ended their old association and that whatever he was doing with his life—he still wanted to see her alone, and talk to her.

She could hardly wait for the time to pass. One hour was nothing . . . from eight till nine—yet it dragged interminably. Like the conversation in the common-room, listening while Berry tried to tell Lucie about life at Keynwood. Poor 'Horsey', Lucie thought, she was rather a lonely person and trying so hard to be amiable and helpful, with her broad toothy smile. Lucie hadn't the heart to disappoint her. She listened patiently.

Geoff Mallow appeared to be Berry's favourite among the masters. 'A real person', she called him. It appeared that he was writing a book called *Cricket Through The Years*. Joanna Parrish was terribly nice but reserved and one could never get anything out of her. On and on, Berry chattered, only capturing Lucie's real attention once, and that was when she mentioned the magical name, Nat.

Berry confided on a lower note.

"I believe that Nat had a 'thing' about Joanna at one time. Nobody knows what happened, but whatever it was, it ended at our Christmas party. They hardly ever speak nowadays. Someone told me that Jo can't stand him, and that she snubbed him, so he's cold-shouldered her ever since."

Lucie listened to this, somewhat bewildered. It didn't make sense to her that any woman could want to snub Nat. But she decided that she had better take everything that Berry said with a grain of salt.

Berry went on to tell her about a woman's club in Brighton that she had joined and how she was also treasurer for an old people's home in Horsham; she hoped that Lucie would join the club and help her run some of the summer outings for her 'old dears'. Tactfully but firmly Lucie tried not to be drawn into any of these ventures. Then, because Berry looked so mournful, relented and promised to visit Horsham with her one day when she did not have to go home.

At last nine o'clock struck. It struck with a low, musical note from a grandfather clock just outside the Head's study, and for Lucie it was a mighty sound that reverberated right through her being. She gave a little gasp, jumped up and said to Miss Day:

"Do forgive me . . . I . . . I've just forgotten something I must do."

And then she rushed. Flinging a short coat over her summer dress, she ran out into the garden. There were a million stars in the sky. Keynwood was beautiful on this still night of May. Lucie lifted her face to those cold stars and knew all the mad happiness of expectation—caring little what realisation might prove.

He was there; standing a little back from the swimming pool behind a clipped yew. There drifted to Lucie the aroma of an Egyptian cigarette. She knew that scent so well. Nat always smoked Egyptian cigarettes and admitted that he was extravagant about his tobacco. Now he saw Lucie, threw the cigarette end down and put his heel on it.

"Hullo, there," he said softly.

Lucie stood still. It was as though all the wild excitement that had accumulated in her died down. She must not allow herself to feel this way, she reflected—or give away her feelings so hopelessly. It wouldn't be what Marta would advise. It wouldn't, she felt sure, have the right effect on Nat.

Her voice trembling a little, she tried to speak to him as though she were quite indifferent to the magic and splendour of being out here alone with him under the star-strewn sky.

"Oh, hullo, Nat," she said calmly, and dug her hands into the pockets of her coat. "'Fraid I'm a bit late but I've had a lot to do."

He gave her a long steady look. Then he murmured:

" 'O blessèd, blessèd night! I am afeared, being in night, all this is but a dream.' "

Somehow, she did not know how, she managed to laugh.

"Do you quote *Romeo and Juliet* like this to the Fifth form, Mr. Randall?"

"No, only to you, Matron," he returned, and now she could see the old familiar mocking smile.

"I played Juliet once," she went on, trying desperately to quell the mad beating of her heart. "It was when I was at school. I spoke my lines with *ever* such a lot of feeling, but my Romeo tripped and fell at my feet, and everyone laughed. That quite cured me of being too sentimental."

He shook his head as though to deny that statement. He noted that she was not wearing her glasses. Her eyes looked huge and quite green in the moonlight. He really had forgotten what a pretty, endearing little thing Lucie was. A few moments ago Barbie Friern had asked Nat to sit in her mother's room and watch a T.V. play with her. He had made an excuse and she had been furious. Sometimes when Barbie was angry she amused him, but tonight he had felt a little tired of her. She was so utterly wrapped up in herself and what *she* wanted. It was nice to have Lucie back in his life, really; Lucie who had always seemed to annihilate self and want only what *he* wanted.

Silently he admonished himself.

'Careful, Randall . . . go easy . . . you have some sort of strange power over this girl. Mind how you use it . . .'

Lucie walked nearer the pool.

"I feel like jumping in, it looks so limpid."

"That limpid look," said Nat, "is as deceptive as a woman's eyes. They can look soft and innocent and hide the most sinister depths."

"What an analogy!" she laughed.

"Anyhow, please don't take a header into this pool," he went on, "because it's full of chlorine, waiting for a lot of beastly little boys, and I've got on a good suit so I don't want to have to dive in and pull you out."

"You wouldn't have to, Mr. Randall. I can swim."

He bowed.

"Congratulations, Miss Reed."

They both laughed. Then there was silence. They could hear the sound of music coming through an open window in the school-house, drifting down to them through the trees. The staff, possibly, playing a radio or television. A nightjar screamed discordantly. A dog barked from a neighbouring farm, then silence fell again, Lucie's soul seemed to overflow with emotion and happiness.

'Oh, Nat, Nat,' she thought, 'you don't know how wonderful it is to be with you again and I'm never going to tell you that it is, either!'

She made a little movement as though to peer down into the water. Then she felt his arms pulling her back.

"Don't do that," he said sharply and swung her round to face him.

She looked up into those dark and handsome eyes and felt for an instant as though she was suspended in mid-air. Her blood tingled. She tried desperately to be flippant.

"Unhand me, sir. No matron can allow such familiarity."

"Can't she?" murmured Nat and warmed now to the old, old game which had always fascinated him. There was something so flattering, so exciting about seeing the way those big candid eyes of Lucie's misted over when she was emotional—and to feel the quivering of her limbs. Holding her, he thought, must be like holding the soft, warm, quivering body of a captured bird, and for an instant he had no wish to release her and let her fly into freedom again.

He drew her yet closer and with one hand quickly drew out the clips that confined her hair.

"I always wanted to see your pretty hair down again . . . like this . . ." he whispered, and ran his fingers through the brown silk of it as it tumbled to her shoulders. He added: "Forget that you're the matron, Lucie, and that I'm a master here. Just let us both remember that we are young and together and that last summer was very sweet."

Speechless, she nodded and let him go on holding her . . . closer than she had ever been to him. But mingling with all her other tempestuous feelings came a prescience of danger. Nat was not serious. Nat had never been serious about her. She had come here because she had wanted to be with him again and to make the sort of impact on his life that he had made on hers. But this was dangerous . . . *this* sort of thing. *This* was where Lucie must keep her little head, she told herself. She tried now to draw away.

"Wait, Nat—" she began.

But she got no further because suddenly he was kissing her, his lips warm and urgent against her mouth.

"Darling . . . you're so very sweet . . . darling . . . my little *Santa Lucia*," he kept whispering in between those kisses, "I'm glad you've come to Keynwood. Terribly glad. You love me, don't you, Lucie? You came here only to be near me—*didn't you*?"

8

FOR a moment Lucie had felt herself so ready and willing to surrender completely to Nat's kiss that she could not speak. She could only place her own hands one on either side of his head and draw his head closer. Then sanity returned. All that was sensible and practical in her broke through the dizzy haze of rapture. She shook her head and pulled away, cupping her burning cheeks with those hands which had just now clung so passionately to him.

"No, Nat. This won't do."

"Darling, why?"

"It just won't," she broke in and with every moment became calmer and cooler although her heart pounded until she found breathing almost a pain.

He shrugged his shoulders and pulled a cigarette case from his pocket.

"Well—if that's how you feel."

"It isn't," said Lucie candidly, "but it's how I've *got* to feel."

"Then you didn't come to Keynwood just for me?"

"I came because I wanted a job." She evaded his actual question and made that statement which was half the truth. Now his eyes twinkled and he gave a low laugh as he lit his cigarette.

"Lucie, Lucie . . . is that true? Was it only because of that?"

"What gives you the right to ask me such a question, anyhow?"

"Oh, my dear, are we going to start talking about rights and wrongs?" He frowned.

Immediately she became a prey to all the old tormenting fear that she would lose him—the intense sadness that she had felt when he had gone out of her life. Yet it was plain to her he was not in love the way she was—that to hold and kiss her, and make light love to her was not for him the beginning and the end of things. She was determined to be strong. She looked up into his eyes and said:

"We are tremendous friends, you and I. We always have been. In lots of ways we seem to understand each other and be happy together. Oughtn't we to let it rest at that?"

He felt suddenly chastened by her honesty of purpose and even a little ashamed. He put a hand on her shoulder and pressed it.

"Still my same *Santa Lucia*! You take life seriously, darling. But I don't intend to try and alter you. You're too sweet as you are."

The praise brought her little satisfaction. She felt an immeasurable sadness standing there with him beside the moonlit pool. That moment in his arms had meant so much that it could not be measured in words. She only knew that she had drunk from a well which would continue to leave her thirsty and that she must turn her back upon it. His embrace had spelled sheer delight and been full of burning promise. Surely it must mean *something* to him, too, she thought. Surely one day Nat would learn to love her as she loved him ? For that day she was going to wait. So she adopted a light vein which was far from being a true mirror of her heart's unrest. She even laughed.

"What a way for a matron and a schoolmaster to behave!"

He responded to her flippancy with apparent relief.

"*Au contraire*. I thought it was delightful. Can't we continue on those lines, Miss Reed ?"

"No, Mr. Randall, we cannot."

"You *have* grown up," he said more seriously. "Really, Lucie, I'm rather intrigued to know what has brought this change about. You're so much more poised than you were, my child."

"My child!" She repeated the words with a jeer. "How old do you think I am ?"

"Too old for some things, too young for others . . ." His eyes were twinkling again with the laughter that made him look so extraordinarily youthful and handsome.

He was an enigma, she thought with a helpless feeling. One never knew where one was with Nat. Perhaps that was nine-tenths of his charm. That, too, was how Marta had always told her a woman should be. Alluring and unpredictable. Sy she, Lucie, having allowed that one dangerous embrace, should withhold from allowing another—tonight at least.

"Let's walk together," Nat spoke again. "Just down as far as the playing fields. It's a perfect night—too grand to spend indoors."

"All right," she said, knowing that she ought to have refused. Now he began to talk to her quite casually and coolly, and she asked herself how it was possible he could have made love to her just now with such passion and so quickly slip back on to a platonic footing. Perhaps, she thought, such things were easier for a man than for a girl. Women were more sentimental, and much, much more vulnerable.

He was reminding her of one day last summer when he had driven her up to London from Hove and ordered avocado pear for her as a beginning to their lunch. It was the first she had ever eaten.

"I had mine with a sharp French dressing, and you sprinkled yours with sugar. Typical of a little girl—liking sweet things," he laughed.

"Yes, I remember." Lucie nodded in a voice of indifference, and she wasn't going to let him know how well she remembered that day and that lunch.

It had become apparent to her then that Nat could teach her so much more than she had ever known about good eating and drinking, and appreciation of what he called 'civilised living'. He had seemed to take her whole life between his two hands and change it—making of her a Lucie who had never lived or breathed properly before. Yet had he ever known the difference he had made to her? she wondered. Obviously he hadn't cared. For it was after that day in town that he had driven her back to Hove, had a sherry with Margaret and herself, and then gone casually. And he had never, *never come back*.

For months she had longed to ask him *why*. *Why* he had broken their friendship so completely after that friendly year? But she had been too proud to get in touch with him. She was too proud to refer to it tonight.

Maggie's opinion had been that he was just *that* sort of man. One who could take a thing or a person up and drop them when he was bored. It had been horribly galling to Lucie at the time to feel that he hadn't minded whether he saw her again or not. How she had suffered, trying not to give way to her desire to phone him up, or make the first move to get him back. She could not bear to remember it even now.

All she knew, as she walked beside him that night, was that she was fiercely glad she had taken this plunge and come to his school.

"Were you very angry with me for fading out the way I did?" suddenly he asked, as though reading her mind.

"Why on earth should I be, Nat?"

He gave a laugh which she could have sworn was embarrassed.

"Well, I don't think I behaved too well to you, did I, my dear?"

"Didn't you?" Lucie asked innocently, even though her pulses thrilled.

"Well, I mean . . . you were always very sweet to me and we had had some very good times together and then—"

"Then what?" Lucie was not making things easy for him, full of love and love's resentment.

"I'm afraid I was unkind. I'm rather like that, Lucie. I've always been a restless, dissatisfied devil. The only thing I have ever stuck at is my schoolmastering and although I get bored to sobs at times teaching these little boys, I also find them entertaining—especially when they are like Wynters, who responds to tuition. I get a kick out of it when they do well in my subjects. But it's *faute de mieux*. I have to earn my living, even if it only brings me in a miserable five or six hundred pounds a year."

"Yes," Lucie said, "but there's always your Uncle Henry to wait for, if I remember right. Haven't you got a wealthy uncle?"

Nat shook his head.

"No, my hopes there are fading. I'm not as sanguinary in that direction as I used to be. He has been gambling rather heavily on the Stock Exchange and buying all the wrong shares. Added to which, to my horror, he's on the verge of a marriage. No fool like an old fool, and he's fallen for a girl half his age. If he has a family, nephew Nathaniel will be right out of the will."

"How disappointing for you, Nat. That means you'll have to go on working," Lucie teased him.

He gave her one of his sidelong looks and drawled:

"How wrong you are! I have other plans."

"Don't tell me you've met a wealthy widow or a beautiful heiress and that you, too, are contemplating marriage!" exclaimed Lucie and thought in agony of Barbara whose father owned this school and who had a small income of her own.

For an instant he didn't answer. Lucie held her breath, agonised, in case those flippant sword thrusts had been drawn from the scabbard of reality. Then came his low laugh again, and an evasive reply.

"Oh, I shan't let the grass grow under my feet, Lucie. I never do."

"I'm sure you don't, Nat," said Lucie fervently.

He paused and looked back toward the distant lights from the school-house. They had reached the first playing field which was be-glamorised by the beauty of the night.

"You know I'm growing quite attached to Keynwood. The school is definitely on the up-grade." He suddenly added: "Ah, well—it's good to be with you again, Lucie. I was a fool ever to break away as I did. I always meant to phone you and ask you out again, but work seemed to pile up on top of me, and I thought at the time . . ."

"Thought what?"

"Oh, it's hard to say. Never mind. I just know I was a fool. You're really the most perfect companion and despite your romantic vein—full of common sense. I've missed our friendship. I'm glad to be in contact with you again. I shall come to you with all my troubles. That's what a matron's for—isn't it?"

"Oh, of course," Lucie said lightly.

"You were always a wonderful listener, too," he said.

"And you, a superb talker, Nat."

"Tell me—are you going to enjoy your work here? Is it right for you?"

"I've only had one day at it but I think it's most interesting. I adore the small boys."

As they stood there, he gave her the full gaze of his handsome eyes.

"They'll appreciate that maternal streak in you. I remember how sweet and gentle you can be."

"Well, we ought to turn back now," said Lucie hastily, "I mustn't make things awkward here—I mean as regards our friendship. I haven't really told anybody I knew you so well, and I'm sure Mrs. Friern wouldn't approve of a close friendship between one of the masters and the matron. In a place like this, one has to be very discreet, I'm sure."

"Oh, yes, of course," said Nat vaguely, "of course."

It wasn't cold but Lucie could suddenly feel herself shivering. On the way back she could not resist mentioning Barbara Friern, as though some deep-down spark of jealousy was the impetus.

"What do you think of the Head's daughter, Nat? She seems to be rather interested in you."

"Oh, do you think so?" he asked, in rather a curious voice,

Lucie thought. She immediately regretted having put the question but, once started, had to go on.

"Do you find her attractive?"

"She has marvellous hair—that Titian shade rather fascinates me. It was always beloved by the Florentine masters, wasn't it? Someone like Annigoni ought to paint Barbie."

At once the tiny spark of jealousy flared up and became a scorching fire. She said:

"I absolutely agree. Miss Friern is a witty girl, too."

"She reminds me of myself at times," said Nat with his twist of a smile. "There's often a knife-edge to her so-called wit. We're both rather malicious."

"Oh, you aren't a bit," Lucie said stoutly.

Now he said with genuine warmth:

"That takes me back. You were always my champion during the course of argument, and I didn't always deserve it. I remember one evening at your sister's. She called me a frightful egotist and you tried to impress her that I was a nice unselfish chap. But I'm not, you know, Lucie. You've always been very sweet but Maggie was right. I *am* an egotist."

"So many clever people are."

"Clever?" He gave a short derisive laugh and pulled another cigarette from his case. It almost hurt Lucie to see that familiar pigskin case again; rather brown and smooth with age, with his initials, 'N.C.R.' in one corner. *Nathaniel Charles Randall*, given to him by his mother when he came of age. She remembered him telling her that he refused a more expensive one because he had thought it might have been bought with his stepfather's money, and he had disliked the man. Nat had a queer pride. "It isn't so clever to find oneself nothing more than a resident master in a boys' prep school at my age," he added.

"But you know so much, Nat."

"Knowledge stored up for no purpose, really. But of course," he added, "it would be different if I could run a school of my own."

And that was the first time that she discovered that Nat had it at the back of his mind that he might one day be offered a partnership at Keynwood. It was also the first time that another hateful little snake of a thought wriggled into her consciousness. The thought that perhaps it was not only Barbie Friern's Titian hair that attracted Nat, *but the knowledge that she was the Headmaster's daughter.*

9

SOMETIMES when one is unhappy or worried about things one has a queer, even masochistic, wish to talk about them—keep hurting oneself by the very reference. It was like that with Lucie that night. She dreaded the mere thought that Barbie Friern attracted Nat, but had to go on mentioning her name. She brought it up again.

"Has Miss Friern—Barbie—a boy-friend?"

Anxiously she watched for Nat's reactions. All she received for her pains was a cryptic smile; that slight curl to his lips.

"Maybe, my dear. Who knows? I believe some Swiss fellow was after her in Geneva when she worked for the Conference. She seems to have had one or two so-called boy-friends, but—"

"Yes?" put in Lucie, holding her breath.

"No one in particular—as yet."

"You are in her confidence, Nat, aren't you?"

"Uh-huh . . ." He nodded.

She swallowed. Obviously the two were great friends these days. But Nat didn't say outright that he was her boy-friend. That was something. She felt almost fiercely possessive about Nat tonight. She wanted him to be hers again, as he had been for those few moments by the pool. She left him at the school door with an abrupt good-night.

"Good-night," he repeated and gave her a vague yet sweet smile which melted the marrow in her bones. "I've enjoyed our talk. I must drive you to Hove one day and meet your nice sister again."

Her heart leaped.

"I'd love that, Nat."

The pain of even the casual farewell tore her foolish heart. She could not resist asking, rather coyly:

"Glad I came to Keynwood, Nat?"

"Delighted," he said and put his tongue in his cheek. "As I told you—you're the matron, and it is to the matron all little boys must run when they're in trouble." He gave her a wicked sidelong smile and vanished.

Lucie went up to her bedroom, shut the door, sat down in

front of her dressing table, and buried her hot face in her hands. She tried to calm down. She went over in her mind every moment she had spent with Nat tonight. She believed that she had every chance of making herself indispensable to him if she went about things in the right way now.

She went to sleep that night quite worn out with her emotions, woke early, dressed and went out into the garden for a breath of fresh air before breakfast.

It was cool again—cloudy—instead of the bright cricket weather Geoffrey Mallow had hoped for. She ran into Geoffrey on the way back to the house. They stopped to say, "Good morning." He was wearing a tweed jacket and scarf. What nice hair he had, she thought—rough, curly, the colour of a polished horse-chestnut. He asked how she was getting on. She answered: "Fine." He told her that he had just been feeding his golden pheasants and that the Head was down there at the aviary with little Finch. (Not Jeremy—just Finch. Poor little mites—all called by their surnames, in such a grown-up, masculine fashion. Lucie had to get used to that.)

She expressed surprise that Finch was up so early. She was only just going to call the younger boys now. The first bell hadn't gone yet. Geoffrey said that it appeared that young Finch had dressed and wandered out by himself. The Head had spotted him in the garden while he was shaving and had run down after him.

"Oh dear, have I slipped up?" asked Lucie anxiously.

"No—not at all. You can't be a watch-dog outside the very doors all night." Geoffrey grinned cheerfully and threaded strong fingers through the wind-tossed hair. "The Head knew you weren't on duty."

"Is Finch okay?"

"Perfectly. The Head's terrific with the small homesick breed y'know."

"So I gathered," nodded Lucie.

"When I was down there, the kid was laughing loudly at the antics of the cock-pheasant, which is the bird I originally found injured. Finch will be right as rain after this. It was just waking up to find himself in a strange bed . . . he was struck down by the pangs of homesickness and wandered off."

"Poor little chap."

"Oh, you mustn't take the tribulations of the boys too much to heart," Geoffrey counselled her. "They are tough really, y'know. You ought to have known our former matron. Name of Anna. We used to call her ''ard-'earted Anna'. You couldn't wring a tear out of *her* eye. She believed all small boys to be calculatedly wicked."

Lucie laughed with him.

"I'm sure she was wrong."

"The Frierns are sure of it, too. That's why the Matron left. But don't be too kind. They can take advantage of you, too."

"I'd better go and get my juniors up."

"By the way," put in Geoffrey with his rather blunt, direct way that was tempered by a friendly grin, "D'you play cricket?"

Lucie laughed again, self-consciously.

"Glory! I used to as a kid, and I've had plenty of it on the beach with my nephew, Tim."

"Excellent. I'll enrol you. The staff will be having a match one afternoon. We always do."

"Wot—me?" Lucie asked in pure Cockney, and with pretended horror.

"Definitely. Miss Day, let me tell you, is one of our best wicket keepers."

Lucie giggled.

"Gracious goodness me. All right, I'll play."

"See you later," he said, and sauntered in.

A nice, simple, healthy type, Geoffrey Mallow, she reflected as she raced up the stairs, two at a time, to see to the small boys' ablutions. Not complex like her fascinating, maddening Nat. Why, oh why, couldn't she have fallen for a sportsman like Geoff who had, she was sure, no dark hidden corners or secret passions—none of the complexities that went to make up Nathaniel Randall's character.

After that she was busy. She actually enjoyed that second day at Keynwood. It was all a rush and a bit confusing, getting used to her job and remembering all that she had or had not to do. But she was not sorry that she had chosen this job. It was less gruelling and responsible than nursing, although in many ways she regretted the waste of her former training and wished Maggie's illness hadn't disturbed the rhythm, that her year away hadn't broken the threads that bound her to hospital life. But her two years' training would certainly be useful at school.

All through the day the thought of Nat pursued her. She derived little satisfaction from his presence during meals. Most of his attention seemed to be directed at Barbie, although he did take the trouble to nod and smile at Lucie when she first sat down at the table, and at the end of supper, he strolled up to her and said:

"How have you been making out, Matron?"

She answered briefly as though she had never felt the warmth of his arms and his lips. "Nicely, thanks, Mr. Randall."

On her first half-day, Lucie took the bus from Horsham into Hove and went home. She felt a sudden wish to see her half-sister. The children were delighted and fell upon her with whoops of delight. Later, Lucie sat in her old place, cosily, in the kitchen talking to Maggie while she got on with the ironing.

Brunhilda took Angela out and gave Lucie a chance to talk to her half-sister alone. She had half decided to tell Maggie the whole story of Keynwood, including that delirious and unexpected moment with Nat by the swimming pool, but when it came down to facts, she couldn't. She was almost afraid. Just as one might be afraid to show the world a priceless treasure, lest it be snatched away. She wanted nothing to spoil her memory of Nat that night. It was a talisman against even the fear that he might be a little in love with Barbie.

She told Maggie about everybody else; how nice Geoffrey Mallow was; how much she liked Joanna Parrish; what a dear Berry Day was, despite her constant threats to draw Lucie into her toils, and interest her in good works. In the end, inevitably, Maggie questioned her about Nat. When Lucie answered, Margaret looked with penetrating gaze at her young half-sister's face. She was a little surprised to find a mask drawn over it. Usually Lucie gave herself away. Margaret said:

"You're hedging, honey. You haven't really told me how things are going with your friend, Nathaniel."

"There's nothing much to report," said Lucie, lowering her gaze.

"Oh, well," Maggie licked a finger and touched the hot iron which gave a little sizzle, "so long as you don't let him break your heart all over again, good luck to you."

"I don't intend to let anybody break my heart," said Lucie airily.

"I think I like the sound of Geoffrey Mallow," was Maggie's summing up, after Lucie stopped talking.

"Yes, he's a terribly nice man," Lucie agreed. "Wrapped up in his nature studies and sport."

"He seems to have made several efforts to be friendly with you."

Lucie got up and stared out of the window from which she could just see a glitter of blue sea, this warm summer afternoon. She said:

"Perhaps. And I'll probably ask him along to meet you one day. He's a reserved type. I know Dick would approve of him."

"Which he didn't do of Nat Randall," Maggie reminded her sister, ironing vigorously.

"I've always understood Nat. You two never have," said Lucie loyally.

The elder girl eyed Lucie's straight young back at the window with affection, and some concern. She was sensitive to the feelings of others and she was positive that Lucie had not told her everything and might bring fresh sorrow on herself in doing this job at Keynwood. Maggie did not trust Nat Randall. The telephone bell suddenly rang.

"Answer it, ducks," said Maggie.

Lucie went into the hall and picked up the receiver, remembering Nat . . . remembering those awful days a year ago when she used to wait for this very phone to ring, hoping that it would be *he* who called . . . tumbling into the depths of despair because it was always somebody else.

Her heart seemed to turn over when, now, in actual fact she heard that familiar charming voice.

"Is that you, Lucie?"

Her face and throat burned.

"Yes, Nat," she said breathlessly.

"I rather gathered you would have gone home as it was your day off."

"So you remembered Maggie's number . . ." Lucie tried to giggle but it was a weak effort.

"*Your* number," Nat corrected her. "Well—it just so happens that a few moments ago a girl-friend of yours—a Miss Rivers—turned up to see you here at school. I met her outside in the drive. I told her I thought you'd be in Hove. She seems to be staying with friends not far from Keynwood and borrowed a car to nip over to see you. I've offered to bring her into Hove in my own car because she says the Jag she borrowed is too heavy for her. She doesn't want to take it on to Brighton. Would you like me to drive her in to you?"

Lucie felt a wild thrill of elation.

"Of course I'd like it!" she exclaimed before she could restrain herself, and only afterwards wondered how Maggie would receive Nat Randall. But how wonderful to think that darling Marta was in Sussex and that she would see *her*. "Please, do come over quickly!" added Lucie.

Now the telephone receiver appeared to have been taken from Nat's hand. Lucie heard the voice of her friend.

"Is it okay by you, Lucie, sweetie?"

"Marvellous, Marta darling. How are you?"

Marta lowered her voice.

"Fine. Listen. Your boy-friend's just gone out to get his car. I don't think I'd have managed to get to you except for him. I can't tackle this enormous Jag one mile further. I didn't have time to let you know I was coming. It was a last-minute decision."

Lucie bit her lip.

"Marta, darling, just for your benefit, Nat *isn't* my boy-friend. And don't for heaven's sake say anything indiscreet to him. The situation's rather tricky."

Marta gave an amused laugh.

"So I gathered from your letter. I'll be tactful. And I must say he's *divine* to look at. I'll tackle him and sow a few seeds for *you*, darling. Of course, if we don't turn up, you'll know I've fallen by the wayside under the spell of those deep dark eyes. I'm not surprised now that you fell so completely. Guy will have to watch out!"

The two girls laughed together. But Lucie felt no jealousy of her dearest friend. She put down the receiver and rushed to tell her half-sister the news.

She might have been less elated if she could have seen what happened the other end of the telephone wires.

Marta had been using the telephone which was in a small room leading off the main hall. Nat had left her there. She had thought herself entirely alone when she made some of her flippant and tell-tale remarks to Lucie. But it so happened that Barbara Friern had just come in through the front door and had stopped when she found the very pretty and smartly dressed stranger talking on the phone. Her sharp ears had heard every word that Marta Rivers had said.

10

IF ever a young woman was angry, it was Barbara. She did
not allow the unknown girl at the telephone to see that
she had been eavesdropping; she moved on, but waited in the
hall, doggedly, until Nat came round to the door with his car.
Then with a pretence of surprise, Barbie wandered out into
the drive and hailed him.

"Hullo, Nat! Where are you off to?"

He looked a trifle embarrassed. Barbara saw it and all her
muscles tautened. Marta had joined them now. The two girls
sized each other up. Marta had already heard about the Head's
daughter, in one of Lucie's long epistles. Cool and slightly
amused, Marta looked at the red-head, whom she summed up
as being extremely attractive but dangerous. Yes, quiet, demure
little Lucie might have quite a fight for it, Marta thought, if
this was her rival. Barbara on the other hand stared stonily at
the pretty stranger who was introduced to her as Miss Rivers;
noting with an envious eye the beautiful cut of Marta's tie-silk
summer suit, her smart short camel-hair coat, her beautiful
Hermés scarf. Barbara said:

"Were you looking round the school?"

"No, I haven't any small boys—yet," said Marta with a
wicked sidelong glance at the handsome young master who
was opening the door of his car for her, "I'm a friend of Lucie
Reed."

Barbara clenched her hands at her sides. She wasn't getting
any change and she knew it. And she knew exactly where
these two were going. For two pins, she thought, she would ask
them to give her a lift into Brighton and so make things
awkward. But it so happened it was one thing she could not do
because Nat *knew* that she had just come back from Brighton.
She had wished she had never told him this morning that she
had been going there on a shopping expedition. She had no
possible excuse for returning now. She looked hard at Nat. He
threw her what was meant to be an ardent and reassuring smile.

"See you later, Barbie. I'm just running Miss Rivers into
Hove."

'Yes, I'll see you later,' Barbie thought furiously and, turning, marched into the school-house.

As far as it was possible for any girl with Barbara Friern's nature, she was in love with Nat. And it was a nature that did not lend itself easily to love. Passion she was capable of but she was really cold-hearted and a little scheming. During the short time she had spent abroad or away from home, she had had no cause to feel neglected by the opposite sex. Men always 'fell' for Barbie. Sensually she was appealing and she had that kind of wit that amused them—just as it amused Nat.

"You're a bit of a tiger cat," he had once told her. "One never quite knows when the sharp claws will show themselves. It makes life exciting."

Yes, she could excite men but not one, so far, had proposed marriage to her. She was determined to marry Nat Randall. He hadn't as much money as she would have liked but he fascinated her. It was not only because he was so attractive and hard to capture, but because he had a good brain which appealed to her; also her father and mother admired him. It had all seemed 'in the bag' lately. Her father adored her. He knew how she felt about Nat. He had promised to help her 'bait the hook'. There had already been discussions about Hugh Friern taking a partner and it had been made fairly plain to Nat that Hugh would be glad to offer him a partnership, a considerable interest in the preparatory school. This would mean security for the man who became Hugh Friern's son-in-law.

Nat had never actually told Barbie that he loved her, but they had been going out a lot together lately. She had been jubilant—fairly certain that she had got him just where she wanted him; until the beginning of this term. *Until the new matron, Lucie Reed, had come to Keynwood.*

Again and again, Barbara had tried to tell herself that she was half-witted to suppose that Nat would be in the least attracted by that mouse of a girl. But Lucie was in love with him. Of that Barbara was sure. She read it in the young matron's eyes when she saw her with Nat. And she was aware that the two had known each other in the past. That there had ever been anything between them . . . anything more than common friendship . . . had not entered Barbara's head until now, when she had heard what Miss Rivers had said.

Now she knew. She was sure that quite apart from Nat's own feelings, Lucie was on the war path for Nat. Hadn't Miss Rivers actually called him Lucie's 'boy-friend'?

Barbara was trembling with jealousy and rage as she went up to her room. Just wait until Nat got back tonight, she thought. She'd find out quite definitely what was going on and if Lucie wasn't careful she'd be out of Keynwood—quick.

"I'll make Daddy dismiss her. I'll hound her out of the school. I'll do something *frightful*!" Barbara stormed and threw herself across her bed in a passion of tears, the first tears she had shed for a great many years.

Nat, meanwhile, drove happily along the Horsham–Brighton road beside Lucie's best friend. He was being his usual gallant self. He stopped the car on the Dyke in order to show Marta the glorious view, and pointed out Chanctonbury Ring, and gave her a cigarette and lit it for her. He said:

"Lucie didn't tell me that she had such a charming friend. I must be grateful to you for not feeling able to tackle the Jag, and for letting me take you into Hove."

Marta thought:

'He's a wow . . . oh, my poor little Lucie! No wonder she's sunk!'

But as Marta looked across the beautiful sunlit Weald, the gently curving Downs, as seen from here upon the high road, she kept her promise to do what she could for Lucie.

"I'm glad, too," she said, "that I was able to get over to Keynwood to see Lucie, and to meet you. You and she have been great friends for a long time, haven't you?"

"We saw a lot of each other last summer. I've often heard Lucie speak of her beloved Marta."

"Oh, she's a darling and I cherish her, too," said Marta warmly. "We were always devoted."

"But you're not at all alike . . ." Nat's dark handsome eyes travelled over the chic figure and attractive face of his companion. Marta spelt 'London' and sophistication. "But of course," he added, "Lucie is unlike anybody else in the world. She's unique."

"You really think that?" Marta asked with interest.

Nat raised his brows.

"Don't you agree? She's not a typically modern girl. Quite Victorian in fact. Full of ideals, shy . . . very sweet. Somehow in my mind's eye, I always see Lucie in a crinoline, heavily chaperoned. She's extraordinarily unsophisticated."

Now Marta gave Nat a serious look.

"Mr. Randall, I know Lucie well. She's a girl with tremendous character under that shy façade."

Nat smiled. He was not thinking so much of Lucie's character in that moment as the fact that Marta had a most charming back to her neck which was long and slender, and that he wished he dare lean forward and drop a kiss on it.

"Oh, yes, Lucie's full of character," he agreed.

"But she does not show it to everybody. She saves her affections for just one or two special friends. I don't think I'd be betraying her confidence in saying that you're one of them. But I expect you know that, already."

Now Nat looked at the red point of his cigarette.

"I do know it, Marta—if I may call you that."

"Go ahead."

"I always feel Lucie is the perfect companion. I'm devoted to her," went on Nat, glibly.

He was not really quite sure what line to take about Lucie with Miss Rivers. The beautiful Marta! With a sigh, he told himself that it was a pity there were so many fascinating girls in the world. But no good trying to flirt with this one. She had a *fiancé* and she was Lucie's friend, and—he reminded himself with a grimace—he had quite enough on his plate at the moment. He knew precisely how angry Barbie had been when he drove Marta away from Keynwood, and that he had left her in one of her 'moods'. He was not unduly concerned. He knew how to tackle Barbie. It was this Lucie affair which might get a little out of hand, as it had done a year ago. There was no need for Marta to enumerate Lucie's virtues and attractions. He knew them all too well.

Remembering her—he also remembered how he had kissed her down by the swimming pool under the light of that May moon. There had been something particularly sweet and romantic and charming about the episode that persisted in his memory. And he had never really made love to her like that in the old days. What had led him to lose his head over her?

Marta spoke again.

"Lucie is easily hurt, Mr. Randall. That's her trouble."

Now Nat made up his mind which direction he would take. In an earnest voice, he said:

"I know. I know. And as you're such a friend of hers and

I'm so fond of her, I'd like to confide in you, Marta. Please call me Nat," he added.

"Yes, Nat? And anything you say to me will be absolutely confidential."

"Well, if you do discuss me with Lucie at any time—I don't say you will—but *if* you do—please try to make her believe that I adore her but that I don't take life quite so seriously as she does. It's all rather tricky now she's come to live at the school. But I just don't want her to be hurt. You *do* understand what I'm driving at, Marta?"

Marta was experienced enough to know exactly what he was driving at. Her heart sank for Lucie. It had been made obvious to her that Nat was the beginning and end of Lucie's existence, and that to him she meant no more than a charming friend. She would certainly have to warn her, Marta reflected. She wondered if Nat was more serious about Barbara Friern. Marta had not taken very kindly to Miss Friern. If it was going to be a tussle between the girls, Marta would like Lucie to win.

'Lucie must hold her horses and step in at the appropriate moment to put a spike in Barbara's wheel', Marta began to scheme, mentally, on her friend's behalf.

She decided that Nat was worth fighting for. She was feminine enough to feel all his strong masculine attraction as they sat there together in the sunlight, finishing their cigarettes.

"I'm not surprised Lucie is so fond of her friend Marta," Nat said glibly, one arm over the back of the seat and almost touching the girl's shoulders. "This fellow you're marrying—what's his name?"

"Guy."

"Guy's a fortunate fellow."

Marta turned to him, twisting her lips derisively.

"You hardly know me well enough to be a judge of that."

"I can see very well," Nat smiled. "And you are very beautiful."

"And you, my dear Nat, are very smooth for a schoolmaster."

He grimaced.

"Oh, lord, don't place me in the Mr. Chips class."

"Mr. Chips was a good, sweet man."

Nat laughed—his low mocking laugh.

"I am neither, of course."

Marta turned and looked at him—her own eyes mocking now.

"I wouldn't have said so. I wouldn't trust you an inch."

"And rightly," said Nat in a fervent voice.

"But Lucie trusts you. Let's get on, Handsome," said Marta with another low laugh.

He withdrew the sheltering arm and shrugged his shoulders. He could see that Marta wasn't going to 'play'. 'What a cad she must think me,' he thought. 'Yet I meant no harm—nothing remotely serious. I was only being frivolous, I much prefer my little *Santa Lucia* to this piece of sophisticated temptation.'

A quarter of an hour later they were in Hove and being led by a smiling bright-eyed Lucie into her sister's lounge. Now Nat had to exert a little more charm to get past Margaret Callow's antipathy toward him, which he knew had developed because of his behaviour last year. He 'rushed her'. (He had always found that effective with women.) He seized her hand, wrung it, gave her his most disarming smile, and said:

"It's frightfully good to see you again, Maggie. I wonder you have me in the house after the shameful way in which I neglected you and Lucie. I've thought of you so many times. If I'd known you had been so ill I'd have been at the hospital with fruit and flowers. I'm *so* sorry. I wish you'd told me. But you look *wonderful*. More beautiful than ever, if I may say so."

Maggie put her tongue in her cheek. Few men, even Dick, had ever called her beautiful. She had looks of a kind, and a personality. But no woman can be proof against being called 'beautiful'. Maggie had built up a hatred against Nat Randall because of the grief he had caused Lucie, yet now she felt it crumbling. She felt herself melting under the warmth of his gaze. She began to argue with herself that perhaps it hadn't been all his fault and Lucie might have been foolish, and oh! what did it matter? Here he was again and Lucie looked so radiant.

"I'm glad to see you, Nat," said Margaret, shaking his hand.

"And how are your heavenly children?"

That cunning question broke down the last shred of hostility. Maggie beamed. She also remembered how good Nat was with children.

"The little horrors are fine—out on the front with my Brunhilda," she said.

"Here we are again with Wagner opera," Nat laughed. "What a wonderful name for a nurse!"

They were all at ease now. Only Marta was a trifle disturbed,

remembering what Nat had said to her up there on the Dyke.
Lucie 'had it' badly. Her eyes were positively starry. She
looked so pretty today, all pink and glowing and happy. She
had had her hair done in a new way, which made her features
look softer. Darling Lucie, thought Marta, glasses off, too . . .
the vain little thing, although she really couldn't see frightfully
well without them.

Marta linked arms with her friend and whispered:

"Your Nat is dynamite. No wonder you're in pieces."

Lucie laughed and whispered back:

"He *is* attractive, isn't he? Did he mention me on the way
over?"

"Yes. Later take me upstairs to do my hair and I'll tell you
more."

Maggie went into the kitchen to switch on the kettle for tea.
Marta decided that it would be rather tactful to give Lucie a
break and followed the elder sister into the kitchen. Lucie and
Nat were left alone.

He had been leaning out of the window looking down the
road toward the sea.

"One gets just that maddening glimpse of the water from
this house," he began. "Why didn't I bring my trunks and
take a dip?"

"I'm so glad you came over, Nat," said Lucie softly. "Don't
you think Marta is wonderful?"

"She's charming," murmured Nat. "When's she going to
be married?"

"Quite soon."

"He's a lucky chap."

"That's what I say. But I can remember in the old days
whenever we discussed a wedding, *you* always used to pull a
long face and say 'poor fellow', " Lucie reminded him.

He thought how adorably feminine Lucie was when she
screwed her eyes up with laughter, like that. Her cheeks were
geranium pink and hot. He forgot all other women in his life
and thought only of the honey he had tasted on Lucie's lips, and
the disarming way in which she had surrendered to his kisses.

He came across the room, quickly took her hands and touched
each one with his lips.

"It's good to be out of the school and here in your home
again, my little *Santa Lucia*."

She rose to dizzy heights.

"Dear Nat! Tell me—when does Marta have to go back? Did she say?"

"I think she wants to get back to this place where she's a guest in time for dinner."

"We might persuade her to stay here and all of us have a supper party!" exclaimed Lucie excitedly.

Nat opened his lips to say 'yes', but closed them again. He had an uncomfortable memory of Barbara's brilliant angry eyes. He must get back to dinner at Keynwood or there'd be trouble *there* and he did not want serious trouble with Barbie. She was the gateway to something that he wanted . . . more than he wanted any woman. He couldn't tolerate the thought of remaining an under-paid master in a boys' school much longer. Teaching was his profession. As such he enjoyed it. He knew that he was good at it, too. Besides it was the only thing he could do at this stage. But he wanted to get to the top. With Barbara's help he might get there—at Keynwood. Of course, he hadn't actually decided that he would marry her. He wasn't all that anxious to tie himself up. But Barbara was sure-fire and fun to relax with after a day's teaching. She was a challenge to any man. She wasn't always easy to handle, which he also found intriguing. She was the complete antithesis of little Lucie, Lucie who aroused the gentle and more protective side of his nature. And sometimes she roused that cruelty which at times a man feels when he knows that a young girl is deeply, helplessly in love with him.

He said:

"It would have been great fun, sweetie, but I have got to get back to eat at Keynwood, so even if Marta stays on you'll have to count me out."

"Then she'll have to go with you because she relies on you driving her back," said Lucie and looked so childishly disappointed that Nat suddenly bent and kissed one of her warm cheeks.

"Um! . . . it's like touching a sun-warmed peach . . ." he murmured. "How delicious you are, Lucie."

Her heart hammered, and her blood sang.

"How badly can a matron behave when she's off duty?"

"You never seem like a matron to me and you never will."

"Still, Nat, I ought to behave with more circumspection."

"Nonsense, darling. Now listen . . . we must have an evening out together soon. Let's make a date. Wouldn't you like to

see that film that they're all talking about—*Gigi*? Shall I take
you to it?"

"Oh, Nat, it would be lovely. I get every second Sunday
afternoon and evening off—next Sunday."

"Very well," said Nat easily. "We'll go to some cinema even
if we can't get into *Gigi*. Afterwards I'll take you to supper,
then drive you back. We can always creep in at separate
entrances and nobody will know we've been out together."

For a single instant, Lucie thought rather wistfully how nice
it would be if they didn't have to be so deceitful and hide their
affection for one another from the rest of the school. She liked
frankness above all things. But while she was the matron at
Keynwood, she knew she must never display her true feelings
for Nat.

She said:

"I'd love to go out with you, Nat."

"Then, it's a date. Meet me, say, at the Royal Albion in the
lounge at three-thirty p.m. Agreed?"

"Agreed," she said softly, nodding.

It was their old trysting place. It seemed like old times—
before she had been through all the misery of losing him.

She was in high spirits when Maggie and Marta came back,
with the tea.

II

THE little scene between Nat and Barbie was short and
unsatisfactory to them both. As soon as Barbie from her
bedroom window saw Nat's car sweep round the drive and
a moment after he had put Marta Rivers into her Jag, and
said good-bye, Barbie ran downstairs and confronted him.
In her iciest voice she invited him into her father's study to
talk.

The Head at this precise moment was in the gym with an
electrician, discussing trouble in one of the circuits.

Nat whistled cheerfully—most irritating to Barbie—as he
followed her. There was no smile on her face when she turned
to him.

"I've got a bone to pick with you—" she began.

He did not let her finish but leaned forward and planted a kiss, insolently, on the corner of her sulky red mouth.

"Any bone that I can pick with you will be delicious," he murmured and half-closed his eyes in that way he had with women.

Barbie flushed angrily. She was not going to admit that the flippant caress fired her longing to pitch herself into his arms. Oh, this maddening man, Nat, why should he attract her so much more than any other man had ever done?

She went straight into battle. She admitted that she had overheard all that Miss Rivers had said over the telephone to Lucie Reed. She accused Nat of not being straight with her.

"You never told me you had ever been the matron's 'boy-friend' in the past," she finished, using the name as though it had a derogatory significance. "Why?"

Nat lit a cigarette. If there was one thing he disliked it was being spied upon or cornered—even by Miss Friern—and he answered Barbie rather shortly.

"My dear, you're being rather foolish, if you'll forgive me for saying so. I did know Lucie ages ago—and her family. But I am *not* her 'boy-friend'. If Miss Rivers used that term, she did so in the casual way people employ that rather loathsome term these days. It has no special significance, I assure you."

Barbie's face brightened. She calmed down. She began to think she had been rather stupid. She had no wish to annoy this man—of all men. She apologised.

"Sorry, Nat. I was just a bit *bouleversée*, as the French say. I suppose because I suddenly imagined you and the matron—" she paused, biting her lip.

Nat flicked the ash from his cigarette. Now he, too, felt easier and he began to think how beautiful this tall girl was with her Titian hair and her sun-golden skin. Beautiful and crazy about him; just waiting for him to propose marriage to her. Oh, yes, he knew. But he was not yet ready to do that. He wanted to carry on with their rather exciting 'affair' which had such possibilities but left him more or less free. When he was definitely of a mind to join up with Papa and assume a more important status in this school—he would ask Barbie to marry him. Not until then. Her jealousy of little *Santa Lucia* appealed more to his sense of humour than his pity. It really was amusing.

He put an arm lightly around Barbie's shoulders.

"I'm nobody's 'boy-friend'—so don't label me, darling," he begged.

Barbara looked more softly at him now.

"Aren't you even mine?" she whispered, smiling.

"That is the sixty-four thousand dollar question," he laughed, and added: "You're very lovely, Barbie. Don't try and turn my head. I've got work to do. All those horrid little boys to teach tomorrow morning. I really must go and prepare some papers, and please don't couple my name too significantly with Lucie Reed's. Promise."

"Promise," said Barbara.

He left her in a better mood although for Barbara the seeds of doubt had been sown, and remained to torment her a little. As for Nat—he decided that women were a nuisance and a man had to be a past-master of subtlety and tact in order to deal with them. But he prided himself that he had managed Barbie nicely.

Meanwhile Lucie lived on air until Sunday came. But morning and night she thought with excitement and longing of the wonderful prospect of the evening out with Nat. When they met at meal-time or casually in the school, they smiled and spoke like two ordinary friends and co-members of the school staff; little more. But Lucie expected no more. She had agreed with Nat that they must be very careful in the school. Perhaps she read more into his smile—his few words —than really lay in them. To make the time fly more quickly, she flung herself ardently into her work.

She had now been at Keynwood for nearly a month. She grew interested in, and attached to, the boys. They brought her their little woes, both mental and physical, and she attended to them. Cricket was now in full swing with Geoffrey Mallow presiding over the sports. It was a busy month and Lucie had as much as she could do to get through.

Her activities started early—helping to get the juniors up and dressed and down to breakfast which she served with Herta, the Danish maid. Once class began there was bed-making, attention to clothes and linen-cupboard, and mending. The boys broke at half-past ten for milk and biscuits. Later there was the midday meal to preside over. Her two hours off every afternoon Lucie spent out of doors as much as possible. But when it rained, she sat in the common-room or in her own bedroom, reading and writing.

Real peace and relaxation did not begin until the staff met in the Head's dining-room for the evening meal and the boys were safe and sound in bed.

It was all a great responsibility, Lucie found, even though Mrs. Friern was there to help and advise. But she was a difficult, exacting woman and, in some perverse way, seemed to push the bulk of the hard work on to her young matron's shoulders but to want to receive the kudos herself. Lucie had learned to dread Stella Friern's sharp and not always charitable tongue.

On the whole, Lucie enjoyed Keynwood and she had gained a perhaps over-enthusiastic supporter in Beryl Day. Lucie tried not to avoid her, because 'Horsey' plainly needed a friend, and to be friendly was not always easy without getting involved in Berry's hobbies which, frankly, did not interest Lucie.

She realised that living in a school like this was like existing in a special world, apart from others. In a way it enveloped and engrossed and she seemed to have no other life until the rare sweet moments when she saw Nat.

In her quiet moments, she thought mainly about Nat and her immense love for him; the joy of having re-established their friendship. She remembered, also, her somewhat disconcerting conversation with Marta when they were in Hove that afternoon. Marta had warned her that Nat was not going to be easy to 'pin down'. He had admitted to a special fondness for Lucie, but he was not as serious as simple-minded Lucie.

Lucie had then asked her friend and confidante if she thought the game worth while. Was it any use her continuing to try to 'get her man'? Marta had said 'yes' to this, but repeated the warning—that Lucie must not be too serious—she must be subtle—make herself indispensable to Nat and gradually establish in his mind a complete need of her.

"Play a waiting game, watch his reactions and be wise," the experienced Marta told her.

When Lucie had asked what she thought of her real chances, Marta had kissed her and said:

"Plenty, darling. You're so sweet and different. *He* thinks so, too."

To those words, Lucie clung. She played her waiting game happily. She had a glorious memory of Nat's kisses to keep as an armour against all doubts and griefs. And now she had an evening out with him, as planned, to look forward to.

She meant to confirm their time of meeting at the Royal Albion Hotel on Sunday morning when they all returned from church. But when she went in search of him, he seemed to have disappeared. Possibly, she decided, he had gone on into Brighton, direct from church. He had friends there with whom he might be lunching.

She did not allow the weather to depress her, although it was bad today. A wet, windy Sunday that kept the little boys indoors. Small, disappointed faces were pressed to the window-panes, big eyes gazed dejectedly at sodden playing-fields and muddy tennis courts. No matches tomorrow, again, if this persisted.

But a very happy young matron took the bus from Horsham to Hove—rushed home—and after a few words with her half-sister, changed into a pale-blue wool dress and jacket and borrowed Maggie's spring hat—a white straw boater with a stiff blue veil. She was feminine enough to do this despite the rain and wind. She disliked having to wear even a trans-parent macintosh, but was forced to. Then on to her meeting with Nat.

She had to queue at the bus-stop. Despite an umbrella and waterproof, the rain eddied around her legs and ruined her new sandal shoes. A gale was lashing the sea on the Brighton front. It was a horrible day. But Lucie remained radiant. She was going to *him*. In a few moments the marvellous man of her heart would be with her. They would laugh and joke together, sit in a cinema side by side; he would hold her hand, as he used to do months ago, before they parted. Her hungry heart yearned for him. What did the weather matter?

She sat in the loggia of the big hotel opposite the Palace Pier and through the wide glass window watched the Sunday crowds on the promenade struggling against the strong wind, and a ceaseless flow of traffic circling around the Old Steine. Each car might be *his*. Each man who came into the lounge might be *him*. Joyously, Lucie watched and waited.

An hour went by. Nat did not appear. Then another hour. Still he had not come. Now anxiety replaced the rapture of anticipation. She got up and searched the lounge. She went out in the wind and the rain and stared at the traffic in the Old Steine. There was no sign of Nat or his car. She returned to the loggia, feeling slightly sick.

She began to wonder now if he would come. But surely he would . . . it would be too cruel . . . too discourteous, if he just did not turn up. It couldn't be. She made excuses. The car had broken down. (But he could have phoned.) Mr. Friern had kept him at Keynwood. (But he could have phoned from there, too.) *Or had he just forgotten?*

At half past six, Lucie stopped expecting Nat.

Under the smart hat, her small face was pale and strained. Her hands trembled. Her lips trembled, too. Her throat ached with the desire to weep. Her lovely, lovely half-day was ruined. She had to face up to the truth. Nat was not coming. He *must* have forgotten.

At a quarter to seven, when a waiter approached for the third time to ask if he could get her anything, Lucie got up and walked toward the vestibule. She decided to go back to Keynwood. She could not go home and face Maggie and admit that Nat had behaved so abominably. Maggie would only say 'I told you so'.

Now, ironically, the weather cleared. The May sun struggled through the storm clouds and the wet sea-front glittered. The waves continued to pound against the sea-wall but it was warmer and the wind was not so rough. But in Lucie's heart there was the darkness of despair—the misery that only the very young who love deeply, and in vain, can feel.

She tried to choke back her tears.

"Oh, Nat, Nat!" she whispered his name.

Then followed anger. How dared he? How *dared* he not come? She would never speak to him again. It was the last time he would be given the chance to stand her up in such a way!

As she stood there, miserably, angrily wondering when the next bus would leave the Steine for Horsham, a tall, loose-limbed man, bare-headed and wearing a raincoat, came into the hotel. Instantly Lucie recognised Geoffrey Mallow. In a panic, she tried to avoid him but it was too late. He had seen her. His nice blue eyes lit up. He strode to her side.

"Why, hullo, Matron. Well met!" he exclaimed.

She tried to answer him naturally but Mallow's discerning

gaze was quick to note the strained look on the small face and the glimmer of tears in the big soft eyes behind the horn-rimmed glasses.

"All alone?" he asked on a cheerful note.

"Y-yes," she stammered. "W-what are you doing?"

"I took myself for a three mile walk along the cliffs to Roedean—grand sight that rough sea! Then I came in here because, if you want to know, I saw you sitting out in that glass loggia and as you seemed to be alone I thought I'd take a chance and nip in and ask you, if you had nothing better to do, if you'd care to see a flick with me. And have a bite afterwards," he added, rather breathlessly.

She looked up at him. Desperately unhappy and insulted by the thing Nat had done to her, this attention from Geoffrey Mallow came as something like a sop to her pride. He was kind and strong and masculine; and it was nice to think he had bothered to come in here to issue that invitation.

She stamped out the memory of Nat and the agony of the last two and a half hours. She said in a low voice:

"What a lovely idea. Thanks awfully, Geoffrey. I . . . I have nothing special to do. I'd love to come out with you."

12

As they walked out of the hotel into the golden dampness of the evening, Geoffrey Mallow looked at the beauty of the sky, heavenly blue now, streaked still with the grey of the storm-clouds that were rolling away, and he wondered what had happened to the little matron. Such a sad little face; and just now when she had taken off her glasses and wiped them, he had seen her furtively remove the traces of tears from the long childish lashes.

He was hesitant to ask her questions about herself. He was a man who knew so much more about flowers than about women, as he often told himself a trifle ironically. Yet there were whimsical moments in his life when he thought he could see a likeness between women and flowers. With them both, one had to be careful. They mustn't be roughly handled. They were sensitive, if sometimes capricious. But women at times scared Geoffrey—and flowers didn't. That was the difference!

Lucie now kept up a running flow of chatter as though anxious to conceal whatever she was feeling deep down inside. She concentrated on Geoffrey and showed a violent interest in the book he was writing.

"Berry tells me she is typing it for you in her spare time."

"Yes," he said, as they walked along the wet glistening promenade. "That is so. Very decent of her."

"She's a nice person," said Lucie.

"Oh, we're lucky insomuch as we've got a very decent staff," said Geoffrey.

"But I remember," added Lucie with a laugh, "when we first met you warned me not to become too involved."

"Ah! That's my hermit instinct." He joined in the laugh.

"How far have you got with your book?"

"Oh, not very far. No time to write, really, during term. I have just started on 'Cricket In the Eighties'."

"And how are your delphiniums getting on? When I passed the bed the other day I thought the plants looked very green and promising."

"Yes, they should be good this year. I trenched them well. They need plenty of rich loam and you'll see me out with my torch at nights, yanking around for slugs. They adore delphiniums."

"I think I'll take up gardening. Flowers seem to be more rewarding than . . ."

"Yes?" he said, looking down at her as she paused.

"Than people," she said, and now her laugh was hard.

'Ah!' thought Geoffrey. 'She's been let down.'

Lucie was struggling valiantly to keep her thoughts clear of Nat. But the pain of the thing he had done to her this afternoon stabbed her again and again. She could hardly bear it. She heard Geoffrey's quite deep voice:

"More rewarding than many human beings—yes. I agree. Though even flowers at times can turn out to be a poor straggling lot—no matter how much attention one has given them," he said lightly.

"Life's frightfully frustrating," declared Lucie.

"Ah well, if you don't ask too much of it, it isn't too bad."

"Isn't it?" Lucie swallowed. (*Oh, Nat, Nat, did I ask too much of you when I expected you to keep our appointment?*)

Again she tried to drag her mind away from him.

"What do you think about young Olifant?" she asked Geoffrey.

He frowned.

"Olifant," he repeated the name. "Oh yes . . . rather a difficult boy, don't you find?"

"I've been watching him," said Lucie. "He always seems to be getting into frightful trouble and yet I feel there is a lot of good in him. How does one deal with lads like that?"

Geoffrey said that the Head had been discussing Olifant recently. The boy had taken one or two thrashings last term, but always seemed to march around the school afterwards with defiance written all over his face. The Head was concerned. During Geoffrey's classes Olifant behaved atrociously —Geoffrey admitted that. One couldn't seem to hold his interest. To dominate and scare more gentle boys was Olifant's main ambition. But he was definitely *good* at games. The best runner and bowler in the school—keen as mustard —and not unsporting when he lost.

Lucie nodded.

"In fact he has courage—I've seen that. And courage is a thing worth having. It only needs, in his case, to be directed into higher channels."

"Absolutely agreed."

Geoffrey went on to tell Lucie that he knew that Brian's own mother was dead and that his father had married again. The stepmother disliked the boy, and now had a son of her own. So it was obvious that an insecure background and acute jealousy were at the back of most of Olifant's troubles.

Now Geoffrey added:

"Randall, I believe, advocates expulsion for Olifant. But I think it would be a pity. It would just about finish him. One ought to be able to tackle the trouble and bring out what good there is in the young vagabond."

Lucie stiffened as she heard the familiar name, Randall. But she could not resist discussing Nat now.

"Perhaps Mr. Randall isn't very patient with Olifant," she suggested.

(*Oh Nat, I know how impatient you can be. Oh Nat, I know so much about you! Oh Nat, I hate you. I hate you for what you did to me today and I'll never, never lay myself open to such humiliation again. It's all over between us!*)

Geoffrey Mallow had his own ideas about the History and English master. Damn clever chap, Randall—personable, amusing—but Geoffrey couldn't do with him. He was a little surprised when he heard Lucie ask:

"Do you know Mr. Randall really well?"

He answered: "We're colleagues, of course, but outside the school we have nothing much in common. He's by way of being an old friend of yours, isn't he?"

"Yes," said Lucie, and clenched her hands so tightly that her nails dug into the palms.

"Let's see what's on at the flicks in East Street," suggested Geoffrey.

"Oh, I'd adore that," said Lucie, far too enthusiastically, but did not mislead Geoffrey into supposing that she was all that happy about going to a show. Something had certainly 'bitten' the little matron, he thought. She was nervy and unhappy. He thought the best thing he could do was to try and take her mind off her troubles.

They sat through a long film which was boring to Geoffrey because it was full of exaggerated emotion and sugary American sentiment. He smoked a pipe and almost dozed through the story, but hoped that it interested the little matron. Once, when he glanced at her, he was horrified to see two big tears rolling down her cheeks. He focused his attention on the film. They had come to a scene between boy and girl . . . the same old thing, Geoffrey thought . . . frustration and misery . . . the girl saying:

"*I never want to see you again. I know you now for what you are. I wish we had never met . . .*"

'Oh, lord,' thought Geoffrey, 'the little matron's actually affected by this thing. Such is the power of the silver screen! There must be something wrong with me. I'd be more upset if I found one of my delphinium spikes had been broken . . .'

Lucie must be in love. With whom, he didn't know. And it wasn't his business. Yet he felt an irresistible desire to comfort her. This young girl affected him as no other had done, so far as he could remember. She appealed entirely to the protective side of his nature. If she had been hurt, as he supposed, by some chap, he would like to knock the fellow's block off. And now Geoffrey did something which afterwards, when he remembered it, amazed him. He put out a hand, took one of Lucie's, and pressed it. He found it small and soft, that hand. Her fingers twined convulsively around his as though needing his strength. He said nothing. Better to say nothing, he decided, but he kept the hand in his large and capable one until the film ended. Then, grinning cheerfully at her, he bent down and whispered:

"Terrific! Boy's got girl, after all! Happy ending—all according to plan."

Lucie did not reply. The tears had dried on her cheeks. She had stared stonily at the final embrace between the screen lovers. It seemed quite definite to her that her own love story could not end happily. The way in which Geoffrey had held her hand had been very nice and comforting. He was a dear and she felt eternally grateful to him for this moral support which he had unconsciously given to her when she most needed it. But as they came out into the street again—and Geoffrey suggested a meal—she shook her head.

"You go and have one. I'm sure you're hungry. I . . . I think I ought to catch my bus back into Horsham."

"But I shall be most disappointed if you don't eat with me," said Geoffrey, "then I can drive you home."

Lucie's head was aching. The desire to hide herself in a corner and weep was so strong as to be almost overpowering. But Geoffrey took her arm and persisted.

"Please *do* have some supper with me. I hate eating alone and I'm sure you must be hungry."

She shook her head dumbly. Now he spoke again, pressing her arm against his.

"Yes, you are. And Lucie—er—nothing's so bad as it may seem to be, you know," he said awkwardly, clearing his throat.

'It's worse,' thought Lucie, '*much worse* than it seems to be. I've finished with Nat—and I can't stay at Keynwood after this term.'

Nevertheless, despite the dramatics of her thoughts and feelings, she eventually gave way. Geoffrey asked her to choose a restaurant for supper. Now I am going to be masochistic, thought Lucy sadly. I want to eat at the place *he* and I used to love after the theatre. . . .

And Geoffrey found himself sitting opposite the little matron at 'The Harpsichord'. As he sat down, he looked around him with approving eye.

"Charming," he said. Then suddenly frowning: "Now, who told me to come here. Was it Berry?"

"No, Nat Randall, I expect," said Lucy in a bright hard voice.

"Ah, yes . . . so it was."

Lucy also looked around her, her eyes feverish, her heart sick with pain and the wild regret that follows the certain knowledge that a love such as hers can bring only the bitterness of pain and humiliation. In here, in this tiny restaurant, she had in the past so often sat opposite Nat. At this very corner table, she had looked blissfully with him at the menu and followed his advice as to what she should eat and why. He used to bring in a bottle of wine of his own choice. He taught her, also, how to smell the bouquet, to roll the crisp gold of the white wines or the red velvet of the burgundies and clarets around her tongue.

"I like this place," Nat used to say. "You must learn to be a gourmet with me and try John's dishes."

Lucie had learned, and grown to adore the place in her fervent, youthful fashion. It was unique—perfectly run by two men who knew everything there was to know about French food. John cooked. George waited. There were only a few tables. The entire restaurant consisted of the ground floor of one of those old, small houses in Regency Brighton. The walls were papered with red and white damask enriched by soft candlelight. There were one or two paintings, mostly of Italy and a portrait in oils—George's work. Opposite the door, high up in the wall, was a niche that Lucie used to call 'the little shrine'. A shrine to a different work of art arranged each week by the artist. Tonight, it was a street scene in Rome, three-dimensional, like a tiny stage set. Narrow, painted, shuttered houses, slender pillars, sunlight slanting against white broken walls. Geoffrey was enthusiastic about everything.

"One might be abroad here—not in Brighton at all," he said. Then, glancing at the menu, "What about this Chicken Harpsichord which seems to have everything in it from wine to mushrooms and pineapple and so on, Lucie?"

But Lucie was silent, staring at the plate stonily, forcing back the hot tears, her whole being rebelling against the anguish of her memories. Geoffrey was dear, and sweet and kind. But oh, God, she wanted Nat back again. She wanted those old lost days. She bent low, low in her cushioned seat, struggling for control.

'My dear little Harpsichord . . . my dear little shrine . . . oh, God, God, why isn't Nat with me tonight? *Why did I ever come back?*'

Geoffrey was a good companion—not nearly as blunt as he sometimes appeared in school. Yet, after Nat, he bored her—frankly she admitted that to herself. But she promised to go out with him again and offered to take him along to meet Maggie and the children.

Later in the evening outside the school-house door, Geoffrey bade her good-night and thanked her for what he called her 'charming company'.

"I'm so often alone—it's been a real pleasure," he said.

She felt genuinely pleased and thanked him warmly in turn for the whole evening. He had done much to restore her *amour-propre*, she thought; so much more than he knew. And she went on to tell herself that Nat Randall wasn't the only man in the world.

Immediately there came the stinging and devastating thought:

'But he is . . . *he is* . . . I like Geoffrey but *I love Nat*. I love him and oh, I hate him. I never want to see him again!'

But as she walked through the school, quiet and deserted at this hour, her gaze sought him everywhere. She told herself that if she should come face to face with him she would cut him dead, she would walk right past him . . . she would show him that she was finished . . . that he couldn't treat her like that.

But she didn't meet him. She only saw Herta who greeted her with a smile and told her that the boys were all asleep and everything was peaceful.

"You haf had a goot time, Matron?" Herta asked.

"Oh, splendid!" said Lucie, with a brilliant smile.

Then to her bedroom . . . and, alone at last, she relaxed, and with a little whimper, like a creature who finds its hurt intolerable, she flung herself on the bed and buried her face on the crook of her arm.

That night, she cried herself to sleep.

She woke with a splitting headache next morning and went downstairs looking pale and heavy-eyed, but with a dogged determination to be strong and not to let anybody—least of all Nat—know how badly she was feeling.

The bell had not yet rung to waken the boys and start the

hum and buzz of a new day. Because of her headache, Lucie decided to take a stroll round the gardens and have a look at Geoffrey's precious flowers. She was not going in the direction of the swimming pool . . . no—she wouldn't remind herself of the night when Nat had met her there, and lifted her to the heights of bliss in that long, sustained embrace.

But she was not to find the morning as peaceful as it looked, with dew-pearled grass, a summer mist over the big chestnut trees at the bottom of the Head's private gardens, and the sound of the birds carolling their early theme of joy. For, from his bedroom window, Nat Randall, half-dressed, had glimpsed the slight figure in the white overall wandering through the grounds. He had just finished shaving. Hastily he brushed his hair, examined his face in the mirror, flung on a grey flannel coat and hurried downstairs.

The sight of that girlish figure, alone and forlorn, had filled him with remorse. He knew exactly what he had done to her yesterday. He felt that he must talk to her before the day's work began.

Lucie had only walked as far as Geoffrey's bed of delphiniums when she heard that familiar voice.

"Lucie!"

Startled, she swung round. Her cheeks flamed when she saw Nat. The blood seemed to rush through her body. She set her teeth to meet what she felt sure was going to be an unpleasant encounter.

"Lucie," Nat repeated the name, and in an intimate way, with all the old charm in his handsome eyes, caught at both her hands. "I saw you come here. I'm so glad. I wanted a quick word before the day starts."

She flung away his hands as though they burnt her.

"I don't think you should risk being seen with me, Mr. Randall, should you?" she said icily.

"Don't be silly, darling."

"Please don't call me that."

"Now Lucie, I know you must be annoyed with me, but—"

"Annoyed with you!" she broke in, and wrenched off her glasses so that he could see the way her eyes blazed. "I feel more than annoyance. I feel absolutely the biggest fool on earth for ever having kept our appointment. I might have known *you* wouldn't keep it! Well—you're the first man I've ever waited for—for three solid hours—and you'll be the last."

"Lucie, I'm damned sorry. I do apologise—"

"Please don't bother," she broke in. "Save your breath."

"Lucie, give me a chance to explain—"

"There can't be any explanation. If something happened that stopped you from meeting me, you could have phoned through to the Albion and asked them to give me a message. That's the beginning and the end of it."

Now Nat bit his lip and frowned. He was pretty good at wriggling out of difficult moments and calming down irate females. He had had a certain amount of experience. But he really had no good excuse to offer Lucie. It was Barbie's fault, of course (not that she knew it) but she had got hold of him during the afternoon and asked him to accompany her and her parents to Warnborough—a boys' prep school near Dorking. It was a school of considerably higher standing than Keynwood. The Headmaster, Alec Oldfield, was very friendly with Hugh Friern.

The Frierns had been asked to dine with the Oldfields. It had been suggested that Nat Randall should go along with them, to make up the fourth. He had accepted the invitation without giving a second thought to the one he had issued to Lucie at Maggie's house. His head had been full of himself and his future. Oldfield was an influential man, worth culti-vating, and it was the first time Nat had been asked to a private party at Warnborough.

He had remembered his date with Lucie during the very middle of dinner. He had confessed himself 'put out'. He did not want to be so gratuitously rude or to insult Lucie. He consoled himself with the thought that if he didn't turn up, she wouldn't wait too long, and that he would make it up to her as soon as he saw her again. Then he had forgotten about her. He had told one or two witty stories after dinner, been a great success with Mr. Oldfield, and been laughingly informed by Barbara on the way home that Mrs. Oldfield had called him the most attractive man she had met for a long time.

He had felt warmed, well-fed and flattered and held Barbie's hand in the car, driving back to Horsham. Then after her parents had gone upstairs, she had lingered to say good-night and he had permitted himself the pleasure of kissing her. Her lips had clung to his. Her beautiful, rather hard face had looked quite soft in the starlight and the kiss had been longer than he had intended. When it ended, Barbara had whispered:

"I think you know what this means to me, don't you, Nat?"

He had told her that he did and left her with the sure knowledge that Barbie was in love with him. Her lips had been attractive and yet . . . what he had felt for her had been, he knew, mere passion—the promise of the things he wanted for himself in the future.

Strange, but she did not have the same intoxicating effect upon him that *this* young girl, his *Santa Lucia*, seemed to have when he held her in his arms. He made an effort to reinstate himself with Lucie.

"Darling," he said, "I'm going to be very honest with you. Something rather important came my way and I clean forgot our date. There! I've admitted it. Not many men would be so honest. I haven't tried to fake or excuse. I behaved atrociously. And when I remembered—it was too late."

"Much too late," said Lucie with a short laugh.

"I'm damned sorry," Nat repeated, "I couldn't apologise more."

"I don't want you to. It doesn't interest me."

"Don't be ungenerous, darling."

"And please do stop calling me 'darling'."

He lifted an eyebrow sardonically, now took a cigarette from his case.

"So I'm to be excommunicated from *Santa Lucia*'s favours, am I?"

She drew a deep breath. His apology could not compensate her for the ghastly fact that he had just *forgotten* to meet her. Her pride revolted when she remembered the agony of mind she had suffered in that hotel, waiting for him. He looked madly attractive this morning, (as always!), she thought, standing there, smiling in his rather ironic, half-bantering way, expecting her to forgive him and throw herself into his arms, no doubt. But she wasn't going to do it. Now she burst out:

"It really doesn't matter whether you met me or not. In actual fact, while I waited at the Albion I decided that I was wasting my time and that one can't really take up the threads of an old friendship so easily."

"Now you're just being cross and childish—" he began.

"You can say what you like," she interrupted, "but I think

I made an error of judgment in taking this job at Keynwood. However—what I do or don't do in the future is not *your* affair."

"Look, Lucie, I've made my explanation and I've apologised," he said. His voice was sullen and his smile had faded.

"O.K. But I'm just not interested. And now, if you don't mind, I must get back to the boys."

"So you are not even interested to know what I did last night?" he asked, resentfully.

"Not particularly. But no doubt it included Miss Friern."

(*That was a mistake and she realised it as soon as she had said it. Why add to her humiliation by letting Nat think that she was jealous of Barbara Friern?*)

Nat gave a low, amused laugh. It infuriated her.

"Well, in actual fact, I did go out with Barbie, but not alone. We were—"

"I haven't time to hear your story," broke in Lucie, "and I honestly don't care whether you went to the moon with Barbie Friern or any other girl." And she turned and began to walk away. She must be thankful, she told herself, that she had preserved her pride and not allowed that suffocating charm of his to break through her anger. She would never forgive him, whatever excuse he made.

She heard his voice following her:

"Lucie—come back, you little idiot—"

She turned her head and flung an answer over her shoulder.

"Don't waste your time, Nat—at least not with me."

Now he fell back. He was not used to being rejected in such a manner. It half amused him, but only half. He was also annoyed. First of all with himself and secondly with Lucie for daring to refuse him her forgiveness. He stood alone for a moment or two, smoking his cigarette, scowling at the May morning. "Oh well," he reflected, "if that's how Lucie wants it, I won't bother any further."

13

THE weather on Sports' Day at Keynwood was not as good as they had hoped it would be. It was cool, for June, and the sun shone spasmodically. Geoffrey Mallow was disappointed but too busy organising the games and displays to do more than glance doubtfully now and then at the threatening skies.

Hugh Friern and his wife (Stella in her 'best floral') prepared to entertain parents to tea. The boys hung excitedly round the school entrance, awaiting the cars to bring mothers and fathers here for the great day. The entire staff was fully occupied—Mrs. Egbert in her kitchen with her scones and cakes, Herta, Betty and Ann helping arrange tables in the marquee—and several of the prefects, immaculate today in white flannels and blazers and school-caps, were busy making last-minute inspections of the cricket pavilion, the pitch, the jumps, strings and flags and obstacles for the races.

For Lucie it had so far been a gruelling day, what with attending to the outfits of the smallest boys, and running hither and thither at the beck and call of Mrs. Friern who gave orders and countermanded them as fast as they were made. Lucie had learned to her cost that the Head's wife was inclined to do this. Lucie had already had her head 'snapped off ', as she called it, by the fussy, dictatorial woman.

Lucie had only a few moments' peace in which to powder her nose, apply some pale-pink lipstick and smarten up for the great day of the year.

Just before she went down to meet what she knew would be a positive onslaught from anxious doting mothers—all wanting to know how their darlings were progressing—Lucie looked out of her window on to the lawns and playing fields. She felt a certain pride in Keynwood today. It was decorated and important, and the atmosphere was full of subdued excitement. She had already had to comfort little Finch who dissolved into tears because his father had sent a last-moment wire to say he was unable to get down from Scotland in time for the sports. And to issue a quiet word of warning to Olifant.

His father was coming—but with the second Mrs. Olifant—and young Brian, who loathed his stepmother, had threatened to be openly rude to her.

"Everyone expects you to win the hundred yards *and* the high-jump. Don't spoil your day, Olifant," Lucie had begged him.

He had grimaced at her, not without affection. He was no longer rude to the matron these days. He had even expressed the fact that he thought her 'a jolly good sort' but he was still disobedient and truculent and an anxiety to Lucie. Only last evening he had been summoned to the Head's study because he had misbehaved during the English lesson. Nat had reported him.

Lucie thought bitterly of Nat as she looked down on the green lawns, and at the young figures of the boys, walking with some of the parents, to chairs prepared for them under the trees.

It was a month now since Nat had 'stood her up'. A month since they had done more than nod at each other or exchange the odd word in the common-room—both keeping up a pretence of friendship in front of the rest of the staff. Otherwise they had had no real contact. So far as Lucie was concerned, he was as lost to her as though he no longer existed. It was only a fresh pain every time she met him, or heard his voice, or in particular had to watch him smile at Barbie Friern.

She had been sorely tempted once or twice to 'make it up' —to go and tell him she was sorry she had not accepted his apology and forgiven him. She felt, bitterly, that *she* was the loser; that he did not, could not, mind that for the second time their association had so abruptly ended.

But she could not bring herself to lower the flag of pride thus far, and so they remained apart. She flung herself into her job and, in her off-time, either went home (she hardly mentioned Nat to Maggie) or went out with Berry who was delighted to have her. Lucie had also had a picnic in Worth Forest with Geoffrey. He had once again proved himself a charming companion and entranced her by his knowledge of wild flowers, of bird-life, and of all things appertaining to Nature. But no matter what she did, the love that Lucie bore Nat Randall persisted and tore her heart in two.

Sports' Day, as always, proved a great success. Lucie forgot her private troubles for a time and threw herself into the spirit of the occasion. She was kept busy by the mothers (as she expected) and congratulated herself that she had all the answers ready about her little charges. But she watched Brian Olifant anxiously, afraid that the silly boy would wreck his future prospects at Keynwood by carrying out his threat to make a scene with his stepmother.

What happened, she did not know, but was told later by the Head, himself. After the tea, the speeches and the farewells, Hugh Friern sent for the matron and informed her that it had been on the whole a brilliant day, but that Olifant had disgraced himself.

The boy, as anticipated, had excelled at all the sports and received due applause. But his father had left early because Mrs. Olifant had been reduced to tears by Brian's attitude to her.

"I think the end is in sight, Matron—I do not think we can keep him at Keynwood," Mr. Friern announced, and spoke with sincere regret, for he was a man who did not like to expel a pupil.

Lucie pleaded for Brian.

"Please, sir, give him one more chance . . . I know it's all jealousy because of that little brother, and Mrs. Olifant was probably not very tactful."

"People only have a certain amount of time in which to be tactful with small boys, Matron," said Mr. Friern. "Besides, there was that business of Olifant's behaviour in Mr. Randall's class yesterday, as well you know."

"Yes, sir," said Lucie sadly.

"I've just sent for Randall. Whenever I am laid up you know it is he who takes over leadership of the school. He and I shall have to discuss Olifant very seriously."

Lucie was then dismissed. She walked disconsolately into the front hall. For a moment she stood with her back to the notice-board. She looked over the long oak table on the other side, over which hung the head of a stag. It was a twelve-pointer which Mr. Friern had killed. Stag-hunting was one of his pastimes when on holiday in Scotland.

Lucie stared up into the animal's glassy eyes and thought that he looked down on her a trifle scornfully. A proud animal! Stags were reputed to fight to the death, she thought. How proud was *she*? She had weakly given up fighting for her man.

Suddenly she saw the figure of the History and English master coming toward her. How smart Nat was today, with a rose in his button-hole. Busy though she had been, Lucie had noticed what a success he had made with the mothers and sisters who were watching the sports. Her heart jerked as Nat approached her. So, she thought, at the end of this busy social day she found herself alone with him. He did not, as he had lately been doing, ignore her. He actually spoke to her—on a flippant note.

"Still on your high horse with me, Matron?"

Her pulses fluttered. She wished desperately that she did not flush so easily, but knew that her cheeks went hot and pink.

"My, *my*!" added Nat. "You do hate me, honey, don't you?"

She felt stupid and tongue-tied and uncertain of herself. She stared bleakly out of the window. The sun had gone in. There had been one or two rumbles of thunder. Berry had prophesied a storm and now it was about to break. Already heavy drops were spattering against the panes.

Suddenly Lucie dragged her attention back to Nat. She began to appeal to him—not for herself, but for the little boy whom nobody loved, whom nobody seemed to care about in this school, except herself.

"The Head has just told me that you are to have a conference about Olifant. I . . . I would appreciate it, Nat, if you would not be too hard on him."

Nat stared at her, then gave a short laugh.

"My dear, are you continuing to wave a flag in that direction? The boy's hopeless, I assure you."

Lucie started to tell him what she thought about Brian Olifant's psychological reactions to his mother's death and his stepmother's animosity. She added:

"Of course, *you* don't like him, and he is afraid of you. Everything had got on top of him. That boy's been wrongly handled at home. But he is not bad at heart. I know it. He only wants a little understanding and he'd be a different boy."

She saw Nat's splendid eyes darken and his mouth curl in that sneer that she dreaded:

"You really enjoy being a mother to Olifant, don't you, Lucie?"

"Well, there's no need for me to waste sympathy on boys like Wynters, who is popular with everybody, or the twins, who could get away with murder because they are delicate and have to be coddled, or little Finch, whom we all pamper. They're all attractive children and are soon forgiven their sins—Olifant isn't. He started off on the wrong foot here by behaving badly and I don't think you in particular have been kind to him—that's all."

"Anything else?" asked Nat, looking deeply into the young matron's eyes.

"Yes," she said wildly, "what you don't realise is that Olifant is really rather like you, Nat. Oh, not so handsome, or so full of charm, but vulnerable and deeply sensitive because his home life—like yours, as you once told me—went wrong. So he tries to get even with life by snatching everything he can out of it, without counting the cost. He didn't mean to behave badly in class, for instance. He said so. But you goaded him. You do goad people. You drive them away from you, and then snatch them back with all that charm of yours. Olifant's got none and he doesn't get anyone back. He doesn't understand himself or anybody else." Here Lucie added: "If he's expelled from Keynwood, that really will be the end of him. He really will become a psychopathic case."

Nat stood still. He looked at Lucie, amazed by her outburst. His expression made Lucie wish the ground would open and swallow her up. Her moment of proud battle was over and all the natural timidity in her soul, all her love for him urged her to retreat. She was floundering, horribly defenceless, longing to turn and run away.

For a full moment neither of them spoke. Lightning suddenly flashed brilliantly across the hall. It was followed by a peal of thunder. Nat took a cigarette from his case and tapped the end of it. Then he said in a strange, quiet voice:

"More than one storm seems to be breaking over my head. I confess I'm vastly surprised. Not because you've said all these things, Lucie. I like honest people, and you are nothing if not honest. But I resent your personal attack on me. You are thoroughly hostile toward me now, aren't you?"

She wished vainly that she could find words to justify herself, but it was Nat who continued:

"I refuse, anyhow, to admit that you're right about Olifant and I deny that I'm at all cruel to the boy. A little sarcasm never did any pupil any harm, and Olifant always asked for it. However, I'm not going into the question of whether he's a psychopathic case or merely a detestable little boy. But I will say I resent being in any way likened to him. However, we'll let that pass, too. What I *am* going to challenge is that remark you made about my goading people, then trying to snatch them back with my charm. I didn't like the sound of that at *all*."

Lucie felt her cheeks burn. She wished to heaven that the glassy-eyed stag hadn't encouraged her to lower her own antlers and charge at Nat. She gulped:

"I daresay I've said too much. I'd better go. I must see that the dorm windows are closed. It's pouring now."

Before Nat could speak again, Barbara Friern sauntered into the hall. She held a cigarette in a long holder in one slender hand. Her brows went up as she saw Lucie standing alone with Nat. She addressed him:

"Like a glass of sherry, Nat?"

Lucie fully expected him to accept and follow Barbie into her father's room. She was rather surprised when he muttered something about having a job he must do, turned on his heel and left the two girls standing there alone.

Barbara looked rattled. She said something to Lucie which she felt sure was unpleasant but which she couldn't hear because the storm had broken over the school-house in earnest now. The thunder was deafening. Lucie turned and rushed past Barbara up the stairs to the junior dorms, feeling quite hysterical.

The storm persisted right through the rest of that evening. At times there was a lull but the sky remained sullen and threatening and the thunder came back with intermittent heavy downpours of rain. This particularly upset Geoffrey Mallow because it made a quagmire of the flower-beds and was not, as he told Lucie at supper time, at all good for the precious delphiniums.

Lucie tried to enjoy talking to Geoffrey about his plants but she had so much on her mind that he noticed that she answered him only in monosyllables, and that she looked unhappy.

"Sports' Day been too much for you, Matron?" he asked her.

She shook her head and muttered that storms upset her and that she had rather a time getting some of the smaller boys to sleep.

Geoffrey laughed. He told her that in his opinion the boys took advantage of the storm to stay awake and chatter and that they were not really scared.

"Don't you be bamboozled by them, Matron," Geoffrey grinned, in his friendly fashion.

Lucie acknowledged this with rather a sickly smile and took a covert look at Nat who did not return her glance. Neither had he even acknowledged her presence earlier on when she first entered the dining-room. Of course, she thought, he was furious with her for the way she had spoken to him. But she didn't care, she kept assuring herself passionately. She was glad she had been brave enough to tell him a few home-truths, and she thought with deep concern of young Olifant.

The boy had been more than ordinarily difficult to manage at bed-time. She had had to threaten him with bad marks and extreme punishment because he laughed and talked so wildly. But she had noticed the red rims to his eyes and the pallor of the young, defiant face. She was quite certain that Brian anticipated expulsion, and that it would break his heart if it happened. If only these masters would give him a chance!

When she had made a pretence of tucking him up, she had whispered:

"Now do try to behave, Olifant, there's a dear . . ."

But he had given her a bitter, sulky look and whispered back: "All the masters hate me here and I hate them."

"I don't hate you, Olifant," she had said, and her heart had been wrung by the way the boy had blushed and turned his face to the pillow. He had not answered her but she could see from his trembling form that he was crying.

Lucie felt strangely resentful of Mr. Friern and Nat, both of whom, in her estimation, had a blind spot about the boy and seemed unwilling to believe that it was tolerance and understanding—rather than strict correction—that he needed.

At least she noticed that Nat was not being more talkative to Barbie than to anybody else during the meal, for whenever Barbie spoke to Nat he gave her only a cursory answer. Lucie noticed how he frowned and maintained complete silence during dinner—refused the sweet and finally walked out of the room with a muttered apology to the Head. He was in a black mood, she supposed, and she was partly responsible for it. She felt deeply depressed. The gulf between herself and Nat seemed to have widened.

Lightning continued to flash fitfully over Keynwood. Lucie's nerves were on edge. She decided to take a walk alone—to escape from Berry if possible. She wanted to be by herself. She

was quite unprepared when Mr. Friern announced that he
wanted a word with her after the meal.

For a moment she had a horrified notion that Nat might
have told the Head what she had said. Perhaps she was to be
hauled over the coals for trying to teach one of the masters his
place.

But Hugh Friern, alone with her in his study, gave Lucie a
friendly smile and said:

"I thought you would like to know, Matron—since you have
always been so concerned about the lad—that Mr. Randall and
I have decided to give him one more chance."

Lucie coloured. Her eyes widened with surprise and pleasure.

"Oh, I *am* pleased, sir."

"No expulsion this term, anyhow. I am going to have a long
chat with him tomorrow and see if we can start afresh. I shall
tell him that he owes it entirely to Mr. Randall."

"To Mr. Randall!" repeated Lucie, with a jerk of her pulse.

"Yes, it is his opinion that there is enough good in Olifant
to justify a further struggle on our part to tame the little brute.
Which, I may say, I thought rather handsome of Randall con-
sidering what a lot of trouble Olifant had given him, in
particular. Randall has volunteered, personally, to take him in
hand. I'm sure he'll make a go of it."

Lucie made no answer. Her emotions were too conflicting.

The Head continued to speak for a moment. He suggested
that she could add her weight in the effort toward the re-
generation of young Olifant. When she left the study Lucie
felt quite bewildered. It would appear that she had misjudged
Nat. Why, she wondered, had he allowed her to think he
disliked Olifant and wanted the boy to go? She felt guilty,
remembering how harshly she had criticised Nat to his face.

It made some difference as to how she felt about him—not
that it could really bring him any nearer her, she thought
bitterly. He seemed to have gone a long way from her again.

She wished she could talk to Nat and unburden her heart
and see into his. But even if he should appear, she knew she
would turn and run away. She could not face him. It had all
become too complicated and difficult

14

Looking back over the whole affair that night, Lucie came to the conclusion that she could not altogether reproach herself for being gratuitously unkind to Nat about young Olifant, for he, possibly because he just wanted to be argumentative and to disagree with her, had given her the impression that he desired the boy's expulsion.

Being Lucie . . . always generous at heart and quick to forgive (just as she expected to be forgiven) . . . she approached Nat after breakfast. She stopped him in the corridor outside the big room known as 'Hall' which the boys used for recreation. Today, being Sunday, they were free to talk or read there until it was time for church.

Nat turned to Lucie as he heard her call his name. His face assumed a slightly ironic expression.

"Ah, yes, Matron . . . what can I do for you?" he asked, his voice full of exaggerated formality. He gripped the lapels of his coat with fingers and thumbs in schoolmasterly fashion.

Lucie felt hot and embarrassed but blurted out her mind.

"The Head has told me that *you* pleaded for Olifant, Nat. I . . . I was rather rude to you about him, I'm afraid . . . I . . . I'd like to thank you for what you did. I have talked to Olifant," she added, still stammering and blushing, "and he has promised to turn over a new leaf. I'm sure you won't regret it."

Nat bowed.

"I'm glad you're so happy that I have helped return the lamb to the fold. I must say you make a charming shepherdess."

Lucie's cheeks were scorching now. For all her good intentions she felt rebellious.

"Well, that's all I want to say," she exclaimed, and turned to go, but now it was he who detained her.

"Just a moment. I didn't, as you know, take very kindly to your implication yesterday that I had deliberately been unkind to Olifant. Or, indeed, that I take any pleasure in goading anybody. Your pet lamb has done little so far to warrant my special favours. I have had to exercise more patience with him than you realise. However, you seemed so anxious that I should recall certain aspects of my own rather chequered boyhood in order to find excuses for Olifant, I have tried to do so. I *have* a conscience, you know—greatly though it may astonish you."

Lucie passed the tip of her tongue over her lips. She had seldom felt more nervous or at a loss for words with Nat. He had an astonishing facility, she thought, for putting *her* in the wrong. She could think of nothing to say, but just stood there looking, she felt sure, exceedingly foolish.

Tenderness suddenly stirred the heart of Nat Randall as he looked down at her. That was a feeling that certainly no other woman ever roused in him. With Barbie it was all passion, excitement—and future prospects. He was aware of the power he wielded over Lucie. Although she might not realise it, she appealed to all that was best in him. He gave her a smile now that had lost its irony. He even looked what he felt—remorseful.

"You are still angry with me because I behaved so badly to you over our date in Brighton, aren't you ? I said I was sorry at the time. Do you want me to say it again ?"

"I don't want you to say anything!" she blurted out.

"Do you prefer the cold war to continue, then, my dear Matron ?" Nat returned to the old sarcasm.

She shook her head violently.

"I don't understand you, Nat. I never will. It isn't any good our trying . . ."

But suddenly he felt the desire to reconquer her—to master that elusive spirit in the real Lucie, which lay behind all the warm, generous outpouring of her emotions. He said:

"This is stupid. Don't be such a little muggins, my darling. You're off this afternoon, aren't you ? Well, so am I. I've got a date in the evening but I'll take you out in the car somewhere for tea. I'll meet you at the bottom of the drive —other side of the lodge—say at half past two."

Her heart leapt as her whole being responded to this sudden invitation from the one man in the world with whom she most wanted to be. He had called her *my darling*'. It was so like Nat to swing from one mood to another. She never did know where she was with him. It both maddened and fascinated her. She wanted to be proud and to refuse the invitation. She had sworn never to let herself be drawn back into that mesmeric web that he had spun for her. Yet as she looked into those dark, brilliant eyes which were no longer mocking but appealing, she felt as though her very limbs

turned to water. She was lost again, she knew it. She muttered:
"Oh, all right . . ."

"Till then," said Nat softly.

He turned and walked away from her. She fled to the
common-room, angry with herself for giving way and yet
feeling happier than she had done since the awful night when
she had waited for him in vain.

Oh, why did he have this power over her? Why had she
ever come to Keynwood if it was only to be torn in pieces
like this without any real hope of a happy ending?

In her quiet moments alone she always thought of the cool,
even scathing things she would say to him when they next
met; how plainly she would show him that he had no control
over her emotions whatsoever; and that she was quite capable
of keeping her integrity and remaining complete mistress of
herself. Well, it was easy to do those things when he was
being horrid, but when he looked at her as he had done just
now, and his voice took on that low, rich note of appeal . . .
her good intentions just went to pieces.

"I'm ridiculous," she told herself, "just hopeless where
Nat is concerned; but I don't seem able to help it."

And why should she, she further argued, if he wanted to
be friends again—*real* friends?

She saw him again both going to church and coming back.
He gave her a quick nod and smile which heartened her. She
didn't even mind because Barbie, who looked particularly
handsome in a new summer suit, lingered by the lych-gate
to chat to Nat. Lucie walked on with the little crocodile of
boys, winding down the street from the church back to
Keynwood. She did not really know and could not even begin
to guess what terms Nat and Barbara were on. Barbie had
everything in her favour—that was obvious; and what had
she, the matron, Lucie asked herself with some humour,
except two-penn'orth of hope? But she tried to forget Nat
and to interest herself in the chatter of the boys whose main
topic of conversation was yesterday's sports, and the next
big day which would be the Fathers' Match, in a few weeks'
time.

The sun was shining when they got back to the school-house.
There was a good odour of the Sunday roast coming from
the kitchen. The boys poured into the corridor in which
they hung their caps, changed their shoes, and as the older

ones went their way, Lucie had the usual few moments of attending to the younger crowd who needed supervision. Hands must be washed and hair brushed before lunch. There was always plenty to do but it seemed a long, long morning to Lucie who was now watching the clock until half past two. She wanted so badly for that hour alone with Nat. She longed to restore the balance of friendship between them. She had been so terribly unhappy since the Brighton episode. She felt that she could not wait until their meeting at half past two.

She deliberately avoided his eye, drinking coffee in the common-room after lunch, but when she heard him talking to Barbie, Lucie gave a little secret smile and thought:

'He's taking me out to tea, *me* . . .'

It was one of the bitter moments of her life when, just as she was about to rush up to her room to get ready for her outing, Nat followed and told her that the afternoon was 'off'.

"This time it's not my fault, Lucie. I'm really most disappointed," he said.

She blinked at him, feeling the blood rush to her cheeks then drain away. Such was his power over her. She was plunged at once from joy into misery . . . that sick, *sick* little feeling of disappointment; of utter frustration.

"Oh, why?" she breathed.

Frowning, he explained.

During lunch, Hugh Friern had asked Nat if he was doing anything today and when he had said 'yes', that he was going out to tea, the Head had then asked if it was at all possible for him to cancel the date. It appeared that a Mr. Arkwright, a local architect, wanted to come over to Keynwood that afternoon to discuss the plans which were afoot for building a library and reading-room for the older boys. At the moment, the school boasted of only one small inadequate room and as Keynwood had a particular reputation for classical education, and there were at the moment a great many surplus books for which they had no place, it was necessary to give the older boys more facilities for choosing and digesting books of reference in peace, rather than to have to join the rowdy throng in 'Hall'.

"I know," Nat told Lucie, "that this scheme is very dear to the Head's heart and he thinks I ought to be in on it because I'm the History and English master. Apparently Arkwright has to go to Oxford tomorrow and will be away some days, and he thought the Head might like to get the plans approved and so start the building. You see," Nat added, still frowning, as though irritated by the whole affair, "we cleared the last financial fence yesterday when Sir Mark Finch sent a very generous donation towards the new library."

"I see," said Lucie, in a small voice.

"I apologise sincerely," went on Nat, "and you can take it from me that I'm just as fed up as you are. But I just can't very well refuse the Head a request like this. He's quite capable, as you know, when he wants his own way, of asking who I'm going out with and where; so I thought it best not to argue."

Lucie summoned up that side of her which was proud and spirited, and gave a hard little laugh.

"I didn't say I was fed up, did I? Maybe I shall be glad to have the chance to spend a quiet two hours with my book," she said.

She became suddenly desirable to Nat in every way. He had planned a charming and romantic hour or two with her by one of the hammer ponds on this warm, lazy day. The plans for the library here were dear to his heart, of course, but he hated having his own arrangements altered at the last moment.

"Oh well," Lucie spoke again, as airily as possible. "See you some other time, Nat."

Nat glanced over his shoulder, then swiftly from one side to another. There was no one in sight. With a bold gesture he suddenly pulled Lucie through an open door on the right of the stairs, which in turn led through into a smaller room in which the staff hung hats and coats. Before Lucie knew what was happening, she was in the little, narrow dark room that smelled of gum-boots and macintoshes and boot-polish. She found herself in Nat's arms. He held her close—so close that she could feel his heart thudding against her breast.

"Forgive me, *Santa Lucia*. I know I've let you down again but this time it really isn't my doing," he whispered.

She made no answer. She could not. For a moment of delirious excitement she felt his lips brush hers, then return to a long-drawn-out kiss. He was not as heartless as he might seem to her, he thought; he knew what this meant to her. He could not bear the disappointment that had clouded her face. He longed to comfort her. In some strange way it exalted him.

"There!" he whispered, raising his head, "does that show you how sorry I am and how much I would rather have taken you out to tea? I'll make another date . . . watch for a note from me."

"Nat . . ." she began.

But he had released her and gone. The golden moment of ecstasy was over. She leaned back against a pile of coats, shutting her eyes, trembling, trying to restore her composure. Dear life, she thought, she would forgive Nat anything when he kissed her like that. She didn't know where she was with him. Didn't know; didn't care. She was too deeply entrapped by his attraction and her own response to it. She had known no hope a few days ago, and she had almost decided to leave Keynwood. Yet here she was again, back in the grip of the old fever—determined to go through with this thing until all hope of winning Nat's real love was lost.

When she was calm enough to leave that odorous and un-glamorous little room which had become a paradise in a few short seconds, she was laughing at herself. 'Poor silly Lucie,' she thought. 'You *have* got it badly, my dear.' And now back to the delicious torment of watching that pigeon-hole every day for the little note—for the next invitation.

But she was warmly, ridiculously happy again, despite the disappointment over the tea today. In her room, she looked into the mirror, touched with her finger-tips those lips which he had kissed so passionately, and whispered his name:

"*Nat* . . . my maddening, adorable Nat! . . ."

While she was having tea she saw him walking through the grounds with the Head and a young man whom she presumed to be the architect from Horsham. Her gaze followed him blissfully. But her pleasant memories were interrupted by Beryl Day, who was calling her from the window.

"Have you a moment to spare, Lucie?"

Lucie turned to the Geography mistress and smiled gaily. She *felt* gay, and she was always sorry for Beryl, who looked as usual a bit flustered. She held a letter in her hand.

"I've been wanting to tell you about this note I've had from my oldest friend," she said. "But there doesn't seem to have been a chance. It's about my summer holiday."

"Already?" laughed Lucie.

"Oh, the holidays soon come, so one has to make arrangements. And I was all set to do a coach-tour of Scandinavia with this friend. But she's suddenly become engaged and is going on her honeymoon instead of a trip with me."

That left her in the lurch, Berry continued. She didn't wish to go to either of her sisters, as they were both married and made her feel superfluous, so she wanted to know what plans Lucie had made or if *she* would care to 'do' Scandinavia with Berry, at the end of August.

Lucie was embarrassed. Poor Berry, always trying to organise other people's lives as well as her own. Lucie knew that the Geography mistress was staking a lot on her agreeing to this, and she hated to hurt her, but she really could not consider such a holiday. She mumbled something about having to help Maggie with the children this summer and left a downcast Berry to work out her own fate. But, afterwards, Lucie felt badly about it. It seemed sad to be so unloved and unwanted as poor old 'Horsey' who was really one of the kindest and nicest people. It didn't seem fair that one woman should be so good and unattractive, and another—like Barbie—should have all the looks and few of the virtues. The plums of life certainly seemed to drop into Barbie's lap and not Beryl's.

Suddenly Lucie felt very lucky. *She* was not alone. Neither was she unloved and unwanted. She had her family and she had Nat. Or at least she *hoped* that she had Nat!

15

THERE followed a busy week. For Lucie, it meant the usual routine and some extra work in the kitchen because Ann, the younger daily, was off because of illness and they had not found a replacement. Lucie volunteered to help Mrs. Egbert at meal-times (which received somewhat grudging thanks from Mrs. Friern). Lucie had to confess that neither the wife nor the daughter of the Headmaster ever seemed very pleased with her. She did not know why. But she was kept so busy that she had little time to think. The weather was variable but there were plenty of sports to keep the boys healthy and amused. The staff cricket match took place.

Lucie excelled as a batsman and made fifty runs 'not out' which received thunderous applause from the boys. *And* Geoffrey Mallow's hearty congratulations. There was, too, a swimming gala which meant plenty of extra labour for Lucie who had to see that the smaller boys were well rubbed down. There were also the wet bathing trunks to be collected and dried, and all the other tasks which would befall the matron at any boys' school.

On the teaching side, masters and mistresses were kept busy now by preparations for end-of-term exams. Joanna Parrish had two budding musicians among her pupils who were going to take special music examinations. In her spare time, Lucie saw practically nothing of Nat except at dinner in the evening. That note for which she waited was never there in the pigeon-hole. Back she went to the old wretched state of feverish impatience and disappointment every time she ran to look at the 'R's and found nothing for herself except an occasional letter from an outside relative or friend.

Lucie tried to tell herself that it was because Nat was so busy preparing his exam papers that he had no time for 'trysts'. When she caught his eye or spoke to him in the dining-room, he always looked pleasant and had a ready smile for her—but nothing more. When she was alone at night and the long day's tasks were over, she would ask herself in despair if that kiss had meant anything to him—*anything at all*?

It had in fact meant more to Nat Randall than he, himself, realised at the time, but the image of Lucie's transformed young face, with big shining eyes, remained in his mind. He tried to put it aside mainly because he was, as he described it to himself, 'infernally busy' and because his own feelings were slightly chaotic.

If Lucie was on his mind, so also was Barbara Friern, and she was much more to the fore, because she was more easily available than Lucie.

Barbara was growing restive. He could try to stall her but it was obvious that she was not going to be stalled much longer. He would either have to propose to her and have not only Keynwood in the hollow of his hand but an attractive, if exacting, wife; or he would have to resign from this school and start afresh elsewhere.

He was not in an enviable state of mind just at the moment. But to keep faith with Lucie—and his own conscience—he had made a genuine effort to be more considerate toward the boy, Olifant, who used to be his *bête noire*. He had in fact gained ground with Olifant. The boy seemed to be reformed. He now attended the History and English classes with a certain docility and eagerness to learn which he had never shown before.

The 'pep talk' which Nat had had with the boy after Sports' Day had surprised even himself. He had thought, after his years of school-mastering, that he understood the psychology of the average boy. Olifant proved, however, that he was not altogether ordinary. So Lucie had been right. There was something quite decent about the child when one probed sufficiently deep and it would seem he had been suffering (also as Lucie thought) from a genuine inferiority complex which had turned him into the little braggart and ruffian that he had become at Keynwood.

First, Olifant had seemed sullen and answered Nat in monosyllables. But once started on the job, Nat was nothing if not thorough, and he could exercise his charm on both young and old. With patience, with tact and humour, he had finally unwound the boy from the dark cocoon which was smothering his best instincts. Nat even spoke of his own difficult childhood.

"You're not the only one who has had to contend with blows of the kind you suffered when your father married again. My mother also re-married and I loathed my step-papa."

This was where Brian, for the first time, looked at the History master as though he were a human being and not a ruthless machine wishing to crush him.

"I say, sir, did you?" he breathed.

"I did," said Nat, "and what's more, my mamma went off to America and I had to spend my spare time with first one relation and then another, so I know all about the insecure and unhappy sort of feeling such a situation gives one. But I had to fight it and so can you, and the way one really has to look at it is this: your papa and my mamma both got what they wanted and it's up to us to accept the fact and not be thoroughly egotistical and create a disturbance. Taking that line doesn't do any good and merely renders one unpopular and so increases the misery. You get me, Olifant?"

Brian rubbed the back of his head and muttered: "Yes, sir."

"Even when you're older, you can't always have things the way you want them," continued Nat.

"No, sir."

"We're inclined," went on Nat, "to suppose, when we're very young, that when the raps come they're unjust and we're singled out for such injustices. But when one is adult, one soon realises there are raps all the way along the line—for masters as well as pupils, Olifant."

"Yes, sir."

"You're a first-rate sportsman, Olifant. Mr. Mallow takes a good view of you. Why not also direct your sporting instinct to your behaviour here? It isn't exactly sporting to make everybody's life a misery. Do you agree?"

"Yes, sir," said Olifant.

Nat looked thoughtfully at the young flushed face and the thick black hair. He suddenly remembered that Lucie had said the boy resembled him in a way. Well, he had always thought young Olifant rather obnoxious but there *were* likenesses to be drawn—and dash it all, he reflected, things couldn't be easy at home for the poor little brute, with that greedy, unloving, second wife and another kid . . . all designed to upset the boy's equilibrium. Nat said on a kindly note:

"You just decide that you've been behaving like a little ass and show the Head that you think Keynwood a darn fine school and that you want to stay here. That is, if you *do*."

"Oh, I do, sir, I do, I do," Olifant suddenly blurted out, and raised anxious eyes to the master. "I told Matron I did. Matron's been jolly decent to me."

"She *is* jolly decent," said Nat, smiling.

"Oh, I think she's wizard, sir," said Olifant, enthusiastically. "She's the only one I like, because I know she likes me."

"Well, good luck to you, and settle down," said Nat, and pushed off, feeling that he had been somewhat inadequate but that the boy really meant to try. He remembered those childish words:

"The one I like because I know she likes me."

Perhaps he was right. Love begot love. The deep undivided devotion that always seemed to lie in Lucie's big soft eyes called also to depths in Nat's nature which he hardly knew existed. But the very knowledge, flattering though it was, left him in a state of indecision and anxiety. He was anxious because he did not want to do the wrong thing to hurt Lucie again.

He must, he told himself, sombrely, make up his mind one way or the other about Barbie.

Another week and Lucie had almost stopped hoping for that further invitation from Nat. Twice she went out with Geoffrey and each time, whilst liking and respecting him, could not forget the other man. Then one evening when she was least expecting it, as she sat alone in the room in which she busied herself with mending, Nat himself paid her a visit—the first time he had ever done such a thing. She sprang to her feet, as he entered the room, and almost let fall the socks she had been darning.

"Oh, hello!" she said awkwardly.

He gave rather a tired smile.

"Evening, Matron. Got a thermometer handy?"

Her heart-beats quietened down. She could see now how pale he was and the deep shadows around his eyes.

"Aren't you well, Nat?" she asked.

"No, I can't say I am. I've had one hell of a headache all day and I'm a bit shivery. I might be sickening for something. You know the whole district is full of this summer 'flu."

"Don't!" said Lucie, with horror, and ran to fetch her thermometer.

While Nat sat there before her with the instrument in his mouth, shutting his eyes against the light, she watched him with deep emotion. He was, she thought, just like one of the little boys, who came to her for nursing and attention.

She found that his temperature was up to 102° and at once ordered him to bed and gave him suitable tablets.

"Dr. Monk should see you at once," she said.

"Wait till morning before you ring him," said Nat, "I might be better."

"I'm so sorry—" began Lucie.

Now he opened his eyes and gave her one of those warm, sweet smiles which made her his slave.

"Thanks, *ma petite*. I'll be okay."

But she worried about him all night and with reason, for in the morning Nat's temperature had risen and Dr. Monk diagnosed the summer 'flu which Nat had feared.

Mrs. Friern sent for Lucie and ordered gargles for all the boys. All due precautions should be taken. But before another twenty-four hours were over, one of the eleven-year-olds, named Roberts, was tucked up in the sick bay with a high temperature. He and Nat were the forerunners of many others. The epidemic swept through the school.

The twins, always delicate, were the next to follow, then two of the seniors—then little Finch. And Mrs. Friern, herself. Now Lucie had no one to help her, although Dr. Monk said he would send in a night-nurse so that Lucie and Herta could cope with the patients reasonably well during the day-time.

It was a sad disappointment for the school, especially during this fine weather. Outside matches had to be cancelled. No *exeats* were given. Classes were depleted. Lucie soon had the 'san' full, and four dormitories of young patients as well.

It was the sort of 'flu that meant a high temperature for forty-eight hours and an aftermath of lassitude. Lucie, worked off her feet, was desperately tired, but fortunately did not herself fall victim to the epidemic.

Nat, being the first to start, was the first to recover. Then Barbara Friern went down with the infection.

Mrs. Friern sent a message to the matron that night to go and see her daughter.

Unwillingly, Lucie entered Barbara's bedroom. The Frierns had had it done up for her while she was in Geneva. Lucie had only been in it once before, to help Herta turn out, when Ann was off. She did at times give a hand with such things, although Berry always said she was an idiot to do so because it wasn't her job. She had thought then how pretty the wallpaper was—white with blue roses. The divan had a blue chintz headboard to match the gay chintz curtains. There was a grey carpet. It was certainly the most elegant room at Keynwood.

A lamp burned on the table by Barbara's bed. Books, papers, fruit were all there. Lucie could imagine that Ann had seen to that. Young Ann liked to wait on Miss Friern because Barbara put on this 'Continental' air and had brought back one or two attractive dresses from Geneva and was the only person in Keynwood to wear glamorous 'undies' and use perfume. Naturally one didn't expect the delicate odour of *Je Reviens* to mingle with the more masculine odours in a boys' preparatory school. Maggie used *Je Reviens* and Lucie had half a small bottle of her own stored away for special occasions. It was familiar enough to her, when she sniffed the air in Barbara's bedroom.

The patient was sitting up in bed wearing a transparent nylon nightgown—pale grey with narrow shoulder straps over the sunburned shoulders. The red hair was untidy and looked rather wild but beautiful against the pillows. *She* didn't look at all ill. Just rather languid and—grudgingly Lucie had to admit—more attractive in bed than out of it. She must have been manicuring those long pointed nails. They were ruby-red and glistening.

"Oh, hello, Matron," she said in her most drawling voice and looked at her, Lucie thought wryly, much as she would have done at something that had crawled out from under a stone. Lucie, growing hot, could imagine that she did not look very attractive. Her overall was crumpled and stained after the long day's work and she reckoned, too, that her face must be hot and her nose shiny. But she said politely:

"I'm so sorry *you've* succumbed, Miss Friern. Your mother was anxious that I should come and take your temperature."

"You needn't, I've taken it. It's only just over 99° but I came to bed because I thought it was a warning."

"Very wise," said Lucie coolly.

"*You* look a bit crumpled," said Barbara unkindly.

"I apologise for not putting on a clean overall but I was just on my way to bed."

Barbara glanced at her bedside-clock as though to check on Lucie's timesheet.

"So early?"

"It's been a long tiring day," Lucie was driven to defend herself, "and a good many more boys have gone down—as well as your mother. I need some rest."

"Naturally."

Barbara yawned then glanced at Lucie through her lashes. "Did Mr. Randall come down to dinner?"

"Yes," said Lucie.

"How does he look?"

Lucie was staring now, not at Barbara but at a framed photograph which stood on her mantelpiece; one of Nat—which must have been taken when he was at Oxford. He was wearing his college gown. A very young, exceedingly handsome Nat looking straight at one from that photograph with his most elusive mocking smile. Lucie had not noticed it when she helped to do this room. It must be a new acquisition. Presumably Barbara had asked for it and that was the one

Nat had given her. He had certainly never given a photograph to Lucie. The sight of it brought back all the burning jealousy that Barbara Friern was capable of rousing in the younger girl.

"If there's nothing I can do for you, I'll say good-night—" began Lucie.

"Wait a moment," broke in Barbara. "You didn't tell me how Mr. Randall looks."

Lucie set her teeth.

"I . . . didn't really notice."

Barbara's lips curled.

"Didn't you?"

"No," said Lucie, and looked Barbara straight in the eyes.

Whether Barbara believed this or not, Lucie neither knew nor cared. She only knew she could not endure to stand here and discuss Nat further. She was quite sure Barbara was deeply aware of her feelings. Possibly, with some feminine instinct, she had been aware all the way along that Lucie held more than an ordinary regard for Nat Randall, and was determined to crush it mercilessly.

16

LUCIE started to walk towards the door. Barbie called her back.

"One moment, Matron, I don't think I am really going to have 'flu. I feel quite hungry, now. I didn't eat my dinner; so how about bringing me some iced Horlicks? Tell Mrs. Egbert to make it for me."

Lucie's gaze unwillingly travelled again toward the mantelpiece, to that provocative photograph of Nat. *When* did he give it to Barbara? *Why* did he give it to her? Oh! if only she could stop that foolish heart of hers from breaking over trifles like this! But little things could lead to mountains. The very existence of that photograph in Barbara's bedroom was a concrete menace to Lucie's wildest hopes and dreams.

Somehow or other she dragged her attention back to Barbie and told her that Mrs. Egbert had, herself, just retired to bed with a high temperature.

Barbie made a face.

"What a bore!"

"A bore for *her*," said Lucie, rather angrily.

"Who is going to do the cooking?"

"I shall have to cope with Betty until we can get a temporary," said Lucie.

"Oh, so cooking is another of your accomplishments, Matron."

"I wouldn't call it that, but when my sister was so ill I had to do all the cooking for our family."

"You're too good to be true." The sneer was out now in words and Lucie writhed under it.

She did not mean to lose her temper with Miss Friern, but now it flared in revolt.

"Most girls cook!" she exclaimed. "And I don't consider it being 'too good to be true' at all, but maybe if you don't reckon I can cope, you'll come down and cook for the school yourself!"

"You're being a little impertinent, aren't you, Matron?" drawled Barbara Friern.

Lucie went out of the room and shut the door none too quietly. She felt like letting Miss Barbara Friern get up and fetch her Horlicks for herself. She began to wonder if Miss Friern had not gone to bed just in order to have a rest and attract universal sympathy and attention.

Lucie was dead tired and longing for her bed. Unfortunately, she had to stay up another hour before the night nurse relieved her. Lucie tried to tell herself that it was her duty to treat Miss Friern as she did the other patients, whatever she felt about her.

She whisked up the iced Horlicks and took it into Barbie's room—mentally vowing to give away her bottle of *Je Reviens*. Childishly, she had decided that now that she knew Barbie used it, it wasn't going to be *her* favourite scent any more.

By this time, the cat had withdrawn her claws. Barbie smiled and purred at the young matron.

"Poor you, you do look tired! Do get along to bye-byes, and thanks for the drink."

"Good-night, Miss Friern."

"Oh, I think it might be 'Barbie'. Everyone calls me that."

Lucie could hardly bear to use the Christian name but controlled herself sufficiently to do so.

"Good-night—Barbie."

"If I'm normal in the morning, I'll come down and lend you and Betty a hand with the breakfast."

Hastily Lucie suggested that Barbara shouldn't get up until Dr. Monk had seen her. Then it seemed that Barbie could not resist mentioning Nat's name again. As the young matron walked to the door, Barbie said:

"You might ask Mr. Randall to lend me something to read. He was telling me about a new historical novel he'd been given and enjoyed. Will you remind him?"

"I will."

"Matron—" Barbara seemed to have a fervent wish to keep Lucie in her bedroom and gossip. "Tell me—have you got a boy-friend?"

Lucie hoped that across that shadowy room her blush would not be seen.

"No," she answered shortly.

Barbie laced her fingers behind her head and looked at Lucie with sudden benevolence.

"Those overalls are not flattering, but you came down to dinner in a little dark blue number the other night in which I thought you looked quite attractive. Your waist *is* tiny, isn't it?"

"It always has been," mumbled Lucie and wondered what Barbara would have said if she told her that one day in the park, when she was out with Nat, he, too, had remarked on the size of her waist. He had said that he could almost span it with outstretched fingers and thumbs.

"I'm surprised you haven't a boy-friend," went on Barbara, "most girls have."

"Have *you* got one?" suddenly Lucie shot at the other girl, "since we're discussing such things, and if you don't think that I'm being impertinent."

"No, I'm sorry I said that to you just now," murmured Barbara. "I don't really mean to act like the Head's daughter and all that. I'm not really much older than you are, am I? Older in experience, perhaps."

(Undoubtedly, thought Lucie.)

"When you ask me if I have a boy-friend—well I suppose I *have*," went on Barbara lazily.

"I'm sure a great many men admire you."

"One in particular," nodded Barbara, and her gaze went straight to the photograph on the mantelpiece.

Now, without a word, Lucie walked out of the room and quickly closed the door. She could not stay there and be sniped at any more by that hateful girl. For no reason other than sheer jealousy and a new sensation of despair, she began to cry.

Her eyes were blind with the hot, angry tears as she stumbled along the passage, down the stairs and into the kitchen which she imagined would be deserted, because Betty had gone home. She would wait there alone for the nurse to come in to her 'breakfast'.

She was surprised and dismayed to find Geoffrey Mallow at the sink, filling a kettle with water. She remembered then that he had a special fondness for a cup of tea before going to bed. She didn't want to talk to him or let him see her tears but it was too late. He put down the kettle, smiled at her and said:

"*Hello, hello.* What's wrong with you?"

And then Lucie sat down in the big kitchen beside Geoffrey and wept unrestrainedly. She told him a garbled story about 'loving someone who didn't seem to love her' and being afraid 'he was keen on another girl'. It was so unlike her—she was not one to confide in people easily—but Geoff Mallow always had a queer sort of influence over her, as he had had that day in Brighton. He was so calm, so soothing, so human. In fact, while she blew her nose and wiped her eyes, she chokingly laughed at him.

"You do make a marvellous Big Brother, Geoffrey. I've never had one, but I'd like to feel you will occupy that place."

He stuck his pipe between his strong even teeth and grinned. He was sitting now on Mrs. Egbert's huge old-fashioned wooden table which she had refused, during her ten years at Keynwood, to replace with one of those modern unit affairs. He said:

"The trouble is that *this* Big Brother has had little chance of watching you closely, and I believe that is what Big Brothers are supposed to do. I don't really know what my Little Sister has been getting up to."

Lucie blew her nose again. She was calming down. She hadn't, of course, told Geoff more than half the truth. It had been one of those rather dangerous over-cautious confidences. But she could not betray Nat. His story and hers were separate—his life—his loves—were not strictly Lucie's affair.

She couldn't possibly tell Geoffrey that it was *his* colleague whom she loved.

Geoff went on puffing at his pipe and talking in his quiet way.

"Jolly bad luck, my dear Lucie—and if this chap doesn't care for you, very poor taste on his part, if I may say so."

Lucie gazed at him forlornly.

"Nice of you, Geoff—but you see—the other girl is so much more glamorous and exciting."

Geoffrey frowned.

"Do men want glamour and excitement in a wife?"

"It would seem so."

He shook his head.

"Don't believe it. Glamorous, exciting girls are fine to take out to a dinner or a dance, but surely a fellow needs something more when it comes to marriage. You are gentle and reliable and charming. What more does *he* want?"

She choked into her handkerchief.

"Oh, Geoff—it's not true—anyhow—he does want something more, I think. He's ambitious. *She* has a little cash and her—her—father is well-placed too. See?"

She mentioned these facts rather wildly, keeping half an eye on Geoffrey and his reactions, but he didn't appear to guess that it was Nat Randall about whom she was speaking. He took his pipe from his mouth and gave her quite a stern look.

"My dear girl, if your boy-friend is an opportunist of that kind, cut him out. Let him fade. He isn't good enough for you."

Lucie's breast swelled. It was obvious that Geoffrey held her in some esteem and she was gratified. She said:

"You're very kind to me, Geoff, but I must make it plain that I don't ask for perfection and that when I fall in love I'm afraid I fall completely and absolutely. I'm ready to make allowances for—for his—failings."

"Good thing he isn't a schoolmaster. We're proverbially a poor and needy lot," said Geoffrey innocently, unaware of facts. Lucie blushed and stared at the floor.

Geoffrey added:

"Oh, well, given that the fellow's weakness is ambition and that this glamorous, exciting creature *is* out-running you, why not fall back in the race, Lucie? Why exhaust yourself . . for nothing?"

"If we're talking in your blessed sports language, Geoff

do you tell your boys to 'fall out' when they think they're losing, or to make a final effort?"

He made a face at her.

"*Touché!* Okay—go on running till the end. I'll back you to sprint ahead of the other female in time—if you really put your heart and soul into it. You've got such guts."

"Who said so?"

"I did. Big Brother hasn't remained entirely oblivious of all that you do in the school and the spirit in which you do it. You've been marvellous during this wretched 'flu epidemic and you're worn to a shadow, but you won't give in. Okay—don't give in over this love affair. Carry on, and may the best girl win. You, obviously, being the best girl," he added, patting her shoulder.

Lucie felt better. He gave her renewed confidence. She began to smile again. Geoff Mallow was a real person and an idealist. He held Lucie's private belief that people were fundamentally good. He admired the best qualities in human beings—rather than the glittering façade under which there was so often rot, or nothingness. She knew that if she needed a reliable friend, she had one in Geoff. One who would never betray her confidences.

She had felt that when he came to her rescue in Brighton. All through this term she had been made aware of the fact that Geoff Mallow was developing more than an ordinary interest in her. If only she could turn her back on the thought of Nat and find happiness in a man like Geoffrey! Yet she could not stop loving Nat. Her desire for him was like an arrow in her heart. Sitting here alone in the kitchen after Geoff had left her she recalled some poignant lines on the subject by the famous Hazlitt, lines written with tremendous power and emotion over a hundred years ago. It had struck her when she first saw them that they were terrific—momentous—and now she understood what Hazlitt had felt about *his* love after she had left him:

Fragments of the prose haunted her.

'My heart is torn out of me . . . the whole is like a
dream, an effect of enchantment; it torments me, and
it drives me mad. I grasp at a shadow. I try to undo
the past, and weep with rage and pity over my own
weakness and misery . . . Yet the barbed arrow is in

my heart—I can neither endure it, nor draw it out;
for with it flows my life's blood.'

Lucie covered her face with her hands. She could see Maggie
shaking her head at her; Marta shrugging her shoulders;
Berry staring at her, round-eyed, as though she were mad;
the cool, calm Joanna eyeing her scornfully; all these people
would tell her that she was melodramatic about the whole
thing and that what a great writer and poet felt in 1823 could
not be compared with what a young girl—a matron in a
boys' school—could feel in 1960!

But they wouldn't be right, Lucie thought. Even in this
practical machine age, for all its mechanisation, its cold,
calculated approach to sentiment and sex, there was still that
great fount of emotion—the human heart. A heart like hers.
It was the way she felt about Nat Randall. And it was why
she could not pluck out the 'arrow' but must let it go on
transfixing her, still hoping with all her blind passionate hope
that one day he would return her love.

She was roused from her reflections by the sound of men's
voices outside in the corridor, and that in particular of the
Headmaster, calling her:

"Matron! *Matron!*"

Lucie shook her head as though coming up out of deep
water, forced back the waves of fatigue and depression and
hurried out through the kitchen quarters toward the main
hall. She met Mr. Friern and Nat himself. She was quick
to note that the latter looked pale and heavy-eyed. This was,
of course, his first day down after his week in bed.

Hugh Friern gave the young matron the first disagreeable
look she could ever remember receiving from him, and
addressed her in a sharp voice:

"Where have you been, Matron?"

Uncomprehending, she looked from one man to the other
and stammered:

"In . . . in the kitchen, sir."

"Why have you not seen that things were as they should
be in the dormitories tonight?"

Still she could not understand. She saw Nat raise a hand
to his mouth and stifle a yawn. But Hugh Friern, obviously
put out, rapped out an explanation and reproach.

One of the junior boys, Saunders (who had not yet contracted 'flu,) was apt to suffer from sleep-walking. At his parents' wish his window was always kept tightly shut and locked no matter what the weather was like. Lucie usually kept a special eye on him.

Yesterday, as the Headmaster reminded her now, she had found the catch of Saunders' bedroom window broken. She had reported it and Mr. Friern had told her to get Long—one of the men who worked in the school—to mend it immediately. The thing had slipped her memory, so busy had she been and harassed with the constant nursing and rushing from one end of the school to the other. But Mr. Friern was concerned only with discipline and orders. Saunders had taken it upon himself this night, he told Lucie, to walk in his sleep and had been about to climb out of the window and down a water-pipe when, fortunately, Mr. Friern, in the garden for a last 'breath of air', had seen the small figure at the window, shouted to one of the other room-mates to wake up and restrain Saunders—then rushed upstairs with Nat Randall who had been strolling beside the Head on this fine, warm night.

Mr. Friern looked sternly at Lucie.

"But for our intervention you might have had a serious accident on your conscience, Matron. I presume you did not tell Long to mend that catch. It is little things like this that prove one's value and reliability when one is looking after a lot of children."

Lucie was so overcome that she remained tongue-tied. She knew that she was in the wrong. She did not even want to offer the excuse that she had 'forgotten'. It was then, suddenly and unexpectedly, that Nat came to her rescue.

"Just a moment, Head . . . I'm afraid I am entirely responsible. Matron can be exonerated."

"Why so?" Mr. Friern stared at the younger master.

"Matron told me—yes, *me*—about the window and her anxiety for Saunders. She happened to meet me in the hall just before lunch. Do you remember, Matron?" he went on, smiling at Lucie, who looked back at him dumbfounded, "and I said I was going to take my first stroll in the garden and would get into touch with Long. I'm afraid I'm the one who forgot."

Mr. Friern looked surprised but his brow cleared.

"Well, that puts Matron in a better light, certainly. Can't understand you forgetting, Randall, but I suppose we are all extra busy and harassed at the moment. Also, I cannot understand why Matron didn't notice that the catch was still not mended when Saunders went to bed."

Here Nat cut in again quickly:

"I think she fully expected that I would have had it done. I promised to do so because she had so much on her shoulders with all her nursing, and no doubt when the window was shut and the curtains were drawn she thought no more about it."

"Well, we'll excuse it this time," said Mr. Friern on a more amiable note, "and it certainly isn't Matron who is to blame." He added to Lucie: "By the way, we led Saunders into my guest room. He's tucked up in there for the night with the window firmly locked. I'll keep an eye on him, myself, and you can let the night-nurse know what's going on."

"Yes, sir," agreed Lucie, too bewildered to say any more, and turned to fly upstairs—truly disturbed about her young charge. But before she reached the staircase she heard Nat calling after her. She turned and met him with a warm, grateful look.

"It was sweet of you, Nat, *really*, to try and help me out like that, and blame yourself. Why did you bother?"

"I didn't want the little matron to get into a row," he said softly. "After all, you've had rather too much on your small shoulders lately."

"I don't know whether the Head really believed you, but it *was* good of you, Nat."

"I can be good when I want to," he said, smiling and raising one eyebrow in the old mocking fashion.

Her whole heart went out to him. There was so much feeling on that small, tired face that the man felt his own heart go out to her, too. He laid his hands on her shoulders, pulled her toward him, and kissed the top of her head.

"I don't think I could ever bear to see my little *Santa Lucia* in trouble," he whispered, "and now good-night—go to bed and get some rest. I'm off myself. I don't feel too good just yet. Good-night, darling."

Then he was gone, taking with him, she thought, all the joy and warmth and passion that she was capable of feeling. She was immeasurably touched by his efforts to help her tonight. It was just another chain to add to the link that already bound her irrevocably to him. How could she possibly put him out of her life?

17

THE short, sharp epidemic of 'flu was over.
    Lucie found, shortly, that nearly three-quarters of the term was over, too. The final exams were only four weeks away.
    July was a poor month. Many of the school matches had to be abandoned because of heavy rain. The boys grumbled. Lucie, tired out after the session of nursing and doing other people's work, felt permanently languid these days and not very good-tempered, although she tried not to show it. But Mrs. Friern had risen from her sick bed feeling none too well and was a difficult task-mistress. It was, also, obvious to the staff that she was not getting on very well with her daughter, because they snapped at each other at meal-times and bickered about nothing. Only Mr. Friern seemed to keep on an even keel and in his cheerful sensible way did everything he could to 'steady the boat', but Lucie thought that even he looked tired and off-colour. It had certainly been a trying term.
    The head boy, Wynters, all set for a sparkling finish to his preparatory school career, went down with appendicitis on the day of the swimming gala, was removed by ambulance to hospital, and unable to come back. The domestic staff was depleted again and again by illness. But somehow term went on and school routine remained for the most part uninterrupted.
    Lucie—caught up in the web of this new life which seemed to exclude all outside life and have an entity of its own—found time occasionally to face her own personal problems.
    She came down to breakfast one morning and saw at last that little note in the pigeon-hole which she had almost given up hope of receiving. As she tore it open, she wondered why she was not too weary and discouraged to feel such feverish quickening of her pulses. Breathlessly, she read the three lines Nat had obviously scrawled in a hurry.

> *'Believe you are off this afternoon.*
> *Will drive you home. Meet me A.A.*
> *Box. N.'*

Biting lips which trembled with excitement, Lucie pocketed the note and walked out of the hall. So he still wanted to see her—and alone! Since the night when she had talked to Geoffrey Mallow in the kitchen and broken down, her feelings about Nat had remained chaotic—just as Barbie remained a constant menace. But Lucie knew nothing—nothing of how Nat felt about things. Now, perhaps, she would find out at last, she told herself. Perhaps he had asked her out because he had something important to tell her.

She had had her little triumph over young Olifant. For the last few weeks the boy had shown a decided change of demeanour which had resulted in better marks and Olifant, himself, was obviously happier. The Head on one occasion discussed him with Lucie and congratulated her on her efforts. Brian's father had been down to see him and been delighted to find that his first-born was no longer in danger of expulsion. There was even talk of a truce between Brian and his step-mother. Lucie had been most embarrassed to receive an enormous and most expensive box of chocolates tied up with a big satin bow, sent to her with the wealthy Mr. Olifant's thanks for her special care of his boy. When Lucie had protested that she ought not to accept this, the Head had laughed and told her to go ahead and eat them.

"You deserve every chocolate, Matron. And I may say you've more than pulled your weight this term."

"I'm glad to hear *I'm* not going to be expelled then, sir," Lucie had smiled back. Whereupon in his genial fashion Hugh Friern had expressed the hope that she liked her job at Keynwood and would remain. Obviously he had forgotten the incident about Saunders even if she had not.

Her answer had been in the affirmative. But as soon as she had given it, she wondered if she had meant to say 'yes'. Could she ever bear another term—living like this under the same roof as Nat?

It had been raining all morning but cleared after lunch and it was a warm, lush day when Lucie finally met Nat at the place arranged: by the A.A. Box on the main road, just out of sight of the school lodge.

Nat got out of the car when Lucie appeared, and looked at her briefly as he opened the door. She seated herself at his side, carrying with her the big box of chocolates with the pink bow for Maggie's children. She wore no hat. But the light-brown hair had a gleam and sheen in the sun that made an attractive frame for the small, childish face, he thought, but she was looking wan and shadowy-eyed and he told her so. He liked the candy-striped dress and pale pink cardigan. The small waist was even smaller than it ought to be.

"You're incredibly thin—wearing yourself out at that darned school," he said as they sped down the road toward Brighton.

"I'm fine, thanks," she said.

"I think everybody's been knocked up by this 'flu. I know I shan't be sorry when term ends."

"Oh, I think the summer months can be very trying," said Lucie, keeping up the flow of conventional conversation.

But her heart beat madly at Nat's proximity and she hardly dare glance at that handsome profile. He was not in a gay mood, she thought. If only he would *talk to her* and make her understand him!

Nat stuck to formal subjects for a while as they drove through the sunshine. When Lucie asked what he intended to do for his summer holidays, he said that nothing was settled but that the Frierns wanted him to take a fortnight with them in a French mountain resort called Vals les Bains, which was less widely known to the English than most of the spas in France, and where the Head thought both his wife and daughter would benefit by the exquisite air.

"How nice for Barbara!" Lucie exclaimed before she could restrain herself, and then when Nat took a quick look at her and his lips curved in a faint derisive smile, she stared at her lap and felt her cheeks go crimson.

Suddenly he turned the car off the main road into a lane, pulled up under a clump of trees and switched off the engine.

"Have a cigarette, Lucie," he said and held a packet out for her.

She shook her head.

He lit a cigarette for himself and blew a cloud of smoke into the air, frowning up at the blue sky through the haze. Then he looked back at Lucie's childish face and figure. She had taken off her glasses. He lifted them from her fingers and tapped them gently against the back of his hand. He said:

"Lucie, you took on a real job, you know, when you went to Keynwood as matron. You've made quite a mark there, you funny little thing, and it appears to be a thing now that if anyone's in trouble, they go to you. You seem to have plenty of wisdom and consolation to offer one and all. Have you any for me, I wonder?"

"I'm quite sure I don't need to impart any wisdom to the great Nat Randall." She tried to laugh, to still the hammering of her heart.

He added, thoughtfully:

"Off duty you've been seeing quite a bit of Geoff Mallow, haven't you? Have you become his—girl-friend? Or have I no right to ask?"

"You can ask what you like, Nat. But I'm nobody's 'girl-friend', as you call it."

"Not even mine?"

She looked up into the warm, wonderful eyes of this man and felt suddenly furiously angry with him. It seemed impossible for Nat not to try and work that breathless charm of his upon her just when he chose to do so. Was he incapable, she asked herself, of understanding her—or any girl—of realising what he could do to her?

She retorted, through clenched teeth:

"No, not even yours."

"Why should you be," he said, lifting the cigarette to his lips and drawing on it, his eyes almost shut; he spoke half to himself. He added: "Lucie, little Lucie, don't be cross with me today. The great Nat Randall, as you call him, is nothing more than a mixed-up kid, if you really want the truth."

She kept her gaze deliberately from him and stared up at the dusty leaves through which the sun winked and dazzled every time the breeze stirred the tree-tops.

"I can hardly believe that. You always know all the answers."

"Not to *this* one."

"Which?"

"My particular problem, dear Matron . . ." He tried to laugh.

"Have you brought me here to disclose a dark secret?"

"I don't think it's much of a secret," Nat said, with a humourless laugh.

She locked her fingers together so tightly that they hurt. But she maintained her control. Lightly she said:

"Don't tell me. Let me guess. You're in love and I'm going to be the first to hear the name of your future wife."

Now he turned his gaze fully to her, and looking down into the big fine eyes and at the sweet yet strongly moulded mouth, he wished with genuine regret that he had not made such a muddle of things. A man could preserve his independence and consider himself free to charm this woman or that—or have an amusing friendship with one or a more dangerous affair with another; but the time of reckoning must eventually come. And that hour was fast approaching Nathaniel Randall. He knew it. But when he had called himself 'a mixed-up kid' the flippant epithet had not been so far from the truth, he decided. He was mixed up in his mind, all right. In his way he loved this girl Lucie. How much, he was not willing to admit even now. But she had made a deeper mark on him than he had ever expected. That had been made plain to him when he met her again at Keynwood.

But there was still Barbara. And there was all that Barbara meant.

Last night he had spent an uncomfortable hour with the Head's daughter. He had watched a television play—one worth seeing—with the whole Friern family. Afterwards, when her parents had retired for the night, Barbie had insisted on his remaining with her and on dragging things into the open.

It had all started with the discussion about the summer holiday.

"Please promise to come with us to France, Nat," Barbie pleaded.

She had been at her best all the evening—and looking lovely in a cool grey dress with a white fichu which set off the beauty of her flame-red hair. She was fragrant and feminine and altogether appealing to a man. After a long hot summer's day in the classrooms with a lot of exacting schoolboys, there was plenty to attract Nat in the Headmaster's comfortable sitting-room alone with this beautiful girl who was obviously head-over-heels in love with him. He wondered why he had not felt able to go straight ahead and give her the answer she wanted, but had an uncomfortable remembrance of Lucie's soft, serious gaze when he had seen her at supper-time. He had tried to 'hedge' when Barbara pressed him to accept her father's invitation to drive with them to Vals, then Barbara laid her cards on the table.

T—E

"I think it is silly for us to go on with this dissembling, Nat. Why don't we admit that we've fallen for each other? You know Daddy and Mummy won't mind—on the contrary, they want it."

That had made him stiffen and edge away as though he felt the lassoo being tightened around his neck (as Nat always felt when anything or anyone threatened his independence). Yet with the genuine wish to be sincere this time, at no matter what cost to himself, he had shaken his head at Barbara.

"Steady on, my dear. We have a wonderful understanding —as things are—don't let's spoil it all. It would be too awkward, placed as we are, in this school."

But Barbara had lost her head.

"I love you, Nat!" She had said the words with passion and challenge in eyes that were usually cool and not always kind. "You know that. You must have known it for a long time. You're in love with me, too, aren't you? What are we waiting for?"

It had been tempting, all right; devilishly so, he remembered, as he sat beside Lucie under the green boughs. And it should have been so easy to take Barbie in his arms and let himself be carried on the tide of her passion and enthusiasm for marriage and for incorporating him in Keynwood for good and all.

Yet he had still hesitated and that was when Barbara had taken another irrevocable step. She had put her arms around his neck, and said:

"Nat, I want this holiday in France to be a celebration of our engagement. It means everything to me. I think it will mean a lot in the future for you. What do you say?"

18

ALL that was honourable in Nat Randall had led him then to answer truthfully—even at the risk of rousing Barbara's anger.

He took her hands, pulled them away from his neck and looked at her gravely—without that light-hearted mockery which she so often saw in them.

"My dear," he said awkwardly, "this is more than good of you. I'm frightfully touched—"

She broke in swiftly:

"Really, Nat, how frightfully stilted! You'll be saying that you're very *honoured* by my proposal, in a minute."

"I *am* honoured," he smiled.

"Nonsense—you knew I felt this way about you."

"Very well, I knew it," he said quietly.

She caught his right hand between both her own.

"Nat, Nat, why are you like this? What's got into you suddenly?"

"Only the wish to do the right thing."

"This doesn't sound at all like you."

"Am I such an unmitigated cad?"

"Not at all," she said with a short laugh, "but I don't really expect this sort of dialogue from you."

"Dialogue?" He repeated the word and gave a short laugh. "Am I supposed to be speaking my part in a play you've written?"

"Nat, why are you trying to be horrid to me?"

He turned from her, walked to the mantelpiece, leaned an arm on it and stared at the empty grate. How unattractive a grate can be in summer time, he thought vaguely; a dusty electric fire with cigarette ash on it. Soot after the recent storm. Bits of paper. People would use empty fireplaces as though they were waste-paper baskets. Nat had an orderly mind which resented this.

He heard Barbara. She was obviously shaken by the fact that he had not responded in the way she had expected him to do.

"Nat, please, don't let's beat around the bush any more. Have I scared you by offering my hand and heart? Do you, perhaps, think me unmaidenly?"

Now he turned round and smiled at her. Her eyes were brilliant with resentment and her red mouth sulky, but she still looked very handsome and desirable in her cool grey dress with the graceful fichu.

"Barbie!" he protested, "now *your* dialogue is a bit third-rate, isn't it? You know perfectly well that I don't think any unpleasant things about you at all. I'm more than grateful for your proposal, if that's what you like to call it. These are days when a woman doesn't have to wait for a man to say all the things—and he doesn't think any the worse of her for saying them. It's just that I personally am not ready or willing to be tied down for the present."

"You're not really in love with me!"

"I don't know," he said, honestly.

She chewed her lips and pulled angrily at a small chiffon handkerchief which she had tucked into her wide *gros-grain* belt. She said:

"Oh, I know you've often said you weren't a marrying man, but during some of our talks you've suggested that you felt it would be the right thing to get married and to settle down now. You know Daddy is willing to offer you a partnership at Keynwood—and—"

"I haven't been told so officially, Barbie, but if it's the case I'm very flattered."

"What's flattery?" she asked impatiently. "You aren't at all the sort of man to be easily flattered. I think you're trying to tell me you've got something else on your mind. Perhaps concerning another girl. Perhaps there *is* somebody else and I'm not the one and only."

"Barbie, I've never told you that you were."

She went red, then milk-white and he could see her trembling. Was it with rage—because she hadn't got what she wanted—or real distress? he wondered. Did she really love him? Or was she just 'bored' because there wasn't any particular chap around in her life. He didn't know the answer to those questions. What, he asked himself, did any man really know about a woman? They were creatures of such whims and moods. But one thing he supposed he could take for granted: Barbara Friern wanted him for her husband.

"Well—is there another girl?" he heard her demand.

"I don't think I want to answer that question."

"Then there is," she began, her voice rising, "there is. And I believe I know who it is—"

This was where Nat held up a warning hand. He made a quick decision to be strong—stronger than Barbie, or they would head for real disaster. She was going to mention the name *Lucie*. He was sure of it. She mustn't. Too much had been said already. The peace, the even tenor of existence here in the school were threatened by Barbara's hysteria. She was forcing the pace and it was one thing that Nat could not tolerate. With a quick movement he took both her wrists, held on to them, and shook her a little.

"Be quiet, Barbie, please. Don't say any more. I don't want other names dragged into this. It's our private discussion—our personal problem. Please keep other people out of it."

"But you can't deny—" she began again, in a thick furious voice.

He cut in:

"I'm not denying anything, but I don't want you to ask me any more questions. You've been extremely charming to suggest that we should become engaged, and my answer is: thank you my dear—but not for the moment."

"Why don't you say *never!*" Barbara half sobbed the word between her teeth, losing all her control.

"Why do you wish me to be so definite? Why must either of us say anything that we may regret tomorrow?"

She tried to wrench her hands from his.

"You've made it obvious you're not in love with me."

"I'm trying," said Nat, "not to make anything obvious except that I don't want to be pinned down to a 'yes' or a 'no' tonight. Marriage is a thing one's got to think about seriously. It's for ever. I'm not prepared to drop into a church and say 'I will', then later pull out of my commitments in a divorce court. I know you think I'm a hard-hearted sort of fellow with an eye to the main chance—and that may be true. But strangely enough I do believe in the sanctity of marriage."

"Who says that I don't?" Barbara sniffed.

"I'm sure you do. That's why we've both got to be sure. We get on very well and your offer to me carries with it a great deal that I want in life. *But I've got to be sure.* I wouldn't make a good husband if I weren't. I'd be hellish to live with my dear," he added, and, releasing her now, pulled a packet of cigarettes from his pocket and lit one.

She turned away, making an obvious effort to recover herself. Nat went on:

"I owe you a lot. I do thank you, Barbie, but let's talk about this when term ends. Not now. Shall we?"

"If that's the way you want it," she said sullenly.

"That's the way I want it," he nodded.

"I think you're a *devil*."

"My dear Barbara, I am as the song puts it, a 'Very Ordinary Man'."

"Well, I'm no ordinary girl," said Barbara with a strangled laugh, "and I'm not anxious to be stood up beside some other woman, sized up and then given my 'yea' or 'nay'."

He looked away from her and drawled:

"Aren't you being a little vulgar?"

"Aren't you being deliberately cruel when you know what I feel about you, Nat? How can you expect me to like the thought of a rival?"

His eyes warned her again.

"This rival exists in your mind. I'm not thinking of marrying *anybody*, Barbie. I'm a man with many friends and I must be allowed to choose them."

Barbara seemed to know that she was beaten—for the moment anyhow. With a swift change she had stopped snapping at him and drifted into his arms offering her lips with an abandon that he could not resist. He had kissed her good-night as passionately as she demanded. She had left him, whispering:

"I know I'm not perfect but I do truly care for you, Nat. Remember that."

He had gone to bed feeling troubled and thoroughly uncertain of himself but he certainly remembered Barbara's words and that kiss today as he sat beside Lucie in the car. Lucie! *That* had been the unmentioned name. Women were not to be fooled, he thought cynically. Barbara knew perfectly well that Lucie Reed was more than an ordinary friend. *But how much more?* That was the burning question that even he, himself, could not answer, because he wasn't sure.

Grimly he told himself that this was where Nat Randall might be about to learn that he couldn't play about all his life and get off scot-free. If he wasn't careful, shortly he would find himself in an untenable position.

Lucie was baffled by the long silence that had followed her flippant question. She was the first to speak again.

"Come on, Nat. Out with the dark secret."

He realised then that he had been going to tell her the whole story of Barbara and himself but could not. He had no right to repeat any of the conversation that had passed between Barbara and himself last night. He said lamely:

"I've changed my mind. I haven't got a secret to tell."

Lucie felt a jerk of her pulses.

"Then you aren't in love?"

"No," he said shortly.

Lucie folded her hands together. She stared at the knuckles which were white with tension.

She supposed she ought to be glad. But if Nat's denial of love applied to Barbara Friern, it equally applied to *herself*. She said, in a quiet voice:

"Are you in difficulties, Nat?"

"Why do you ask?" he queried, briefly.

"I think I know you fairly well. You are worried."

"Perhaps," he said under his breath.

"And can't I help?"

"Answer me this," he said suddenly. "Do you think I'm in the right environment at Keynwood? That I ought to carry on with schoolmastering in England? Or do you think I ought to drop the whole thing and go away? Join the Colonial Service, for instance, and get some sort of job in one of the Colonies?"

She knit her brows. For a moment, in silence, she watched a black flock of crows circling, cawing, around the top of the tall elms in the field alongside them. Under the green shade of these trees cows stood grazing, flicking their tails against the flies. It was all very rustic and peaceful, she thought. On the whole, this was a lovely, peaceful world. It seemed a pity that today men were so concerned with their turbulent passions and problems that they had little time for the peace and quietude of a country existence. Perhaps that was where Geoffrey Mallow scored. He put Nature before all other things, and made flowers and animals his hobby. He was happy. Once, Lucie used to think it was good for people to read a great deal, to debate, enjoy philosophy and intellectual arguments, be progressive. But she wasn't so certain now. Nat, for instance, lived too much by his books and in his thoughts. It bred complexities. Simplicity —single-mindedness—simple pleasures were what a man really needed. Yet, who was she to advise Nat Randall! How could she ever place this fascinating man of moods and sensuous appreciation of all things civilised into the same category as a man like Geoff?

"Well, what's on your mind, Lucie?" Nat asked her.

She turned and looked up at him with her grave, tender eyes.

"I just don't know what to say, Nat. I can't think of you

apart from Keynwood and teaching—and your enjoyment of the English way of life. You aren't really the Colonial type —if there is such a thing."

"I don't know what I do want out of my life," said Nat abruptly.

With unusual boldness, Lucie suddenly shot a question at him.

"Have you ever discussed it with Barbara Friern?"

She fancied that his cheeks coloured now and he flicked his gaze away from her.

"Why do you ask?"

"I know you—you talk a lot to her—you—you're close friends—" Lucie stammered.

"Yes, I talk to Barbie and we're close friends," he admitted.

"Then have you asked her whether you ought to stay at Keynwood or go abroad?" continued Lucie.

He stared at her, uncertain whether she was deliberately 'getting at him' or quite innocently unaware that she was hitting the nail on the head. Rather angrily he replied:

"I've been asking you what *you* think, not Barbie."

'He is hedging,' thought Lucie, pain wrenching her heart. 'He's more concerned about Barbie than he will admit to me.'

"I'm asking you what *you* think," repeated Nat in a rather violent tone.

"Is my opinion of value?"

"Yes, it is. It always has been."

Her heart began to pound. Her senses swam. She turned right away from him so that he should not see her hot, flushed face. In a low voice she answered:

"Nobody can tell you what to do. Least of all myself."

"Why you least of all?"

That was the instant in which she could so easily have said:

'Because I love you so terribly much. I can't give an un-prejudiced answer. I would hate you to go abroad unless I went with you. I would hate to lose you ever again.'

But she kept silence, her lips compressed. She had the desperate feeling, sitting there in that quiet lane close at his side, that this was a wordless struggle not only for him but between herself and Barbie. She had feared that it might become like this. She and Marta had talked about it and laughed over it. But today Lucie could not laugh. She could not in any sense think lightly or frivolously about Nat and another girl. 'The trouble is,' she thought with a flash of real insight, 'I'm not fit to go into battle for any man. I'm not tough enough. All I want to do now is to run away and hide.'

"So you've no good advice for me, Matron—" she heard Nat say on a lighter note.

She seized the opportunity to answer a little defiantly.

"Not really. But I . . . I'm quite sure Mr. Friern would hate you to leave Keynwood. Now if you don't mind, Nat, I think I ought to get on."

"Get on where? I thought you'd come out with *me*?"

"Aren't we going to Maggie?"

"Do you want to or would you rather have tea somewhere else? Is she expecting you?"

"Yes."

Without another word he switched on the engine, backed the car up an opening into the woods and drove on to the main road again. Lucie felt miserably frustrated. They neither of them spoke until they were well on their way into Brighton. He turned up Windmill Hill and drove over the Dyke. Lucie had so much that she wanted to say and dared not. Nat's own mind was in turmoil. Because he disliked emotional disturbances and had always advocated that a man should remain cool, the master of his fate, and that only a fool allowed himself to be upset or involved with any female unless he wished to be so, he remained grimly silent. He had thought that he could unburden his mind to this young girl who had proved a loyal and devoted friend to him—but he could not.

They reached the crest of the hill. Far below them across the green countryside they could see the blue sea stretching for miles along the sunlit front. Nat felt strangely irritable. The whole situation was provocative and he wanted to end it. When they reached Maggie's little house, he refused to go in with Lucie.

"I'll drop you here, my dear . . ." He looked restlessly at his wrist-watch . . . "I've got to go and see that cousin of mine who lives out at Rottingdean, anyhow. You know the one."

Lucie looked quite frankly what she felt—deeply disappointed. The afternoon had not gone the way she had hoped. She had anticipated a pleasant hour with her half-sister, including Nat, and then tea alone with him. But their conversation had been unsatisfactory in every way. She had learned nothing from him and whatever confidence he had meant to give her he had decided against doing so. She was mystified, except that she was sure he had something on his mind, even if he would not share it with her. She did not really know why he had asked her to come out with him today.

"Well, thank you very much for driving me in, Nat," she said as brightly as she could, "and I'm sorry you won't stay."

"I can pick you up and drive you back . . ." he began.

"I wouldn't hear of it. I can easily get a bus. I haven't any idea what time I'll be going back," she said proudly.

He could see that it would be the easiest thing in the world to persuade her to drive back with him to Keynwood, or even to cut Maggie right out now and go off with him. He wanted her company—her young naive charm and that unspoken adoration in her eyes which had always soothed and warmed him—yet he didn't, just now. He didn't want any woman with him. He felt suddenly out of countenance with the world and himself.

"Don't mind me, Lucie—you know I'm a difficult fellow. Thanks for everything," he said abruptly, and drove away.

She stood looking after the vanishing car. Sunlight and tears together blinded her eyes. She seemed destined to be unhappy either with or without Nat, she thought. As she walked into the house she furtively dabbed a handkerchief at her eyes. She was thankful that the children rushed out and she could hide her feelings by hugging them and joking.

"Auntie Lucie's here!" Angela said ecstatically.

Young Tim straddled his legs and said:

"Look, I've got new shorts, Aunt Lucie, and Mummy's promised me a pen-knife so long as I don't open it when Angela's around."

Lucie gave them the big box of chocolates, which they fell upon with joyous screams. She walked into the kitchen where she knew she would find Maggie. Maggie was there, of course, cooking. What a life—always cooking, washing or ironing, or doing something for the children. Not very glamorous and yet—how lucky she was, thought Lucie. Her beloved Dick was due home next week. Lucie tried to imagine what she, personally, would have felt if this had been her home and these her children, and Nat the husband who was coming back to her from sea.

But the idea was so funny, and seemed so hopeless, that it positively made her laugh. She was laughing when Maggie greeted her.

"Hello! You're in good form, Lucie."

"Oh, I'm fine," said Lucie, pulling off her headscarf.

"Did you come by bus?"

"No—Nat drove me in but he had to go off to an appointment."

Maggie grinned at her half-sister, and lit the inevitable cigarette without which she swore she could not get through the day.

"Ha ha! The Pin-up Boy. What's new, honey? How are things going with him?"

"Nothing new. Everything's fine," said Lucie with deliberate brightness.

But she had to turn her face away because she knew that her eyes were filling with tears again and she could not bear Maggie to see them, or to guess the truth.

19

IT was brilliant weather for Fathers' Day. Another extrabusy day for the matron. A lot of very clean-looking little boys with well-pressed blazers and shorts hung round the cricket pitch that afternoon or strolled around the grounds beside their parents.

Geoffrey Mallow's delphiniums were at their best; tall, graceful spikes in every shade of blue, flaunting their beautiful heads proudly against the dark hedge that flanked the herbaceous border. The golden pheasants strutted up and down their aviary uttering their strange plaintive cries and drew a great deal of attention. The rest of the staff were at their appointed tasks. It was to be tea on the lawn this afternoon after the match.

Berry, who did not care for the heat, and looked scarlet in the face (in one of her most atrocious cotton frocks—striped lemon yellow) hailed Lucie, who was helping Ann and Herta to carry the food out to the long trestle tables.

"Anybody seen our Nathaniel?" asked Berry. "The Head wants him."

Lucie replied that she had not seen Nat. And she bent over her tray thankful that the colour on her cheeks might be mistaken for the warmth of the day. She looked cool and pretty in her white, starched overall, wearing white shoes this afternoon, and she had put more red than usual on her lips. But she felt miserably unhappy; quite out of keeping with the gay appearance of the school grounds and the general air of excitement and anticipation. She had not seen Nat since breakfast and then only to nod to. She had not, in fact, seen him alone at all since that frustrating afternoon when he had driven her home. She knew no more about his state of mind now than she had done before. Anguished and troubled, she watched him whenever the opportunity arose . . . watched and wondered whether he was, indeed, involved with Barbara; watched and wondered endlessly.

But Nat didn't seem to be on the best of terms with Barbie just at the moment. There was far less witty conversation and repartee between them during dinner than there used to be. In fact, Lucie had never seen Miss Friern appear so subdued. Lucie had felt recently that there was an under-current of feeling all the time below the seemingly placid exterior, with all three of them. But nobody gave themselves away. If Lucie did talk at all, either to Nat or to Barbie, it was on a completely impersonal note.

She kept wondering if Nat would write her one of those little notes and ask her to meet him alone again. She kept wondering if she had, for some reason unknown to herself, been pushed right outside the orbit of his mind and heart and would never get back into it again. She slept and she ate badly. One day when she weighed herself in the gym she found that she had lost half a stone since coming to Keynwood.

She began to feel terribly alone.

Dick was home. He and Maggie were happy and engrossed with each other. Lucie had been to see them last Sunday but only stayed a short while. She was not needed there now. When Dick had kissed her affectionately and told her that his little sister-in-law was looking very mature and quite a beauty these days, the praise had brought her little pleasure. Maggie, in fact, without realising that she touched a raw spot, had added: "Our little Lucie is engaged on a big man-hunt. She may come home with a ring on her finger at any moment now." But those words had turned like a knife in Lucie's tender heart. The 'man-hunt', so far as she was concerned, hadn't been very successful, she told herself bitterly. Whatever happened, she didn't expect to go home for the summer holidays with a *ring*!

Even Marta was no longer available to console or advise. Much to Lucie's disappointment, all plans for the wedding in London had changed. Marta had flown out to Malta at a moment's notice to marry Guy over there; so Lucie had even missed the fun of attending the marriage of her best friend.

Now, post-cards came from Malta. 'Blissfully happy', one of them said. 'Thoroughly recommend matrimony', said another. None of them was calculated to make Lucie feel any better. She was glad that Marta had found happiness, but made the discovery, in which she was not alone, that human beings with private griefs are apt to become egotistical, and the very sight and sound of the happiness of others can wound rather than console.

Long before Fathers' Day at Keynwood, Lucie had made up her mind to tell Mr. Friern that she could not return there next term.

Nat came into view a few minutes after Lucie finished laying the tables. He was talking to Sir Mark Finch. Lucie ran straight into the two men, walking through the aperture in one of the tall, clipped yew hedges fringing the Head-master's garden. She looked swiftly at Nat. He returned her gaze unsmiling but stood politely aside to let her pass.

"Oh, hello, Matron," he said.

But Sir Mark Finch stopped her.

"Ah! Just the person I wanted to see. How do you find my young scamp these days? Is he behaving himself?"

Lucie's gaze fluttered away from Nat. She answered:

"He is being very good, really, Sir Mark, and he's tried hard to settle down. No more homesickness."

"I'm most grateful to you for all you've done for him," said Sir Mark. "He seems devoted to you. Mentions you in every letter."

"That's very sweet of him," said Lucie, colouring.

Sir Mark turned to Nat.

"Would it be permitted, do you think, if I asked Matron

to come out with Jeremy on his next *exeat*? I could send
the Rolls for them and I'd like her to see Jeremy's home.
And I know Jeremy's home would like to see *her*," he added
gallantly, with another friendly smile at Lucie.

"I'm quite sure Mr. and Mrs. Friern wouldn't object,"
Nat said shortly.

"Then do come, Matron," said Sir Mark.

For a moment she stayed tongue-tied. She realised the
implication of such an invitation. Mark Finch was a charming,
distinguished young man. His wife was in America. They
were about to be divorced. It might be the forerunner of
many such outings, and not only did it offer the thrill of
driving around in the beautiful Rolls, but of becoming
persona grata in the Finch household, Jeremy clinging to
her (which he was apt to do despite her efforts to toughen
him up). She knew that she ought to be very flattered and
to accept at once. But her large eyes turned to Nat, agonised.
He wasn't looking at her. He was kicking moodily with the
tip of a toe at the pebbles. He looked disgruntled. She thought,
suddenly:

'He couldn't care less . . . *why should I*?'

She said aloud:

"It's frightfully kind of you, Sir Mark, and I'd simply
love to come out with Jeremy."

"Then I'll fix it," he said.

At that moment Jeremy, with a small boy of his own age,
sighted his father and shrieked at him.

"Daddy! Daddy! Wilson Minor says his father can bowl
slow leg-breaks. I bet you can too, can't you?"

" 'Slow' isn't the word," laughed Sir Mark.

Jeremy dragged his father away. For a moment Lucie
found herself alone with Nat. She felt extraordinarily embarrassed and plunged into conversation.

"Isn't it a gorgeous day! Aren't we lucky! I expect Mark
Finch does play a jolly good game . . . don't you think so?"

She stopped, crimson. Nat had raised his eyes and was
regarding her with a touch of irony. He looked, as he always
did on these occasions, she thought, well-turned out and
most attractive. He said:

"We're full of jolly jargon, all nicely learned at school,
aren't we, Matron? Oughtn't I to say something about it
being an awful swizz because I've lost my chewing-gum?"

"If you think that funny . . ." said Lucie huffily.

"I don't think anything's very funny at the moment."

She glanced to the right and the left. Nobody was in sight. Under her breath she said:

"Oh Nat, Nat, what's the matter?"

"Everything," he said.

"Can't I help?"

"No—there's nothing a mere matron can do."

"Have I . . . myself . . . done anything wrong?" she asked helplessly, without pride, conscious only of her overwhelming love for him.

His expression softened.

"You never do wrong, little Lucie. I'm the chap who does and says all the wrong things. I'm just trying to get right both with myself and the world. That's all. Now stop worrying about me and enjoy yourself. I rather think this fellow Finch has fallen for you. He was asking me where you were. There you are! What a chance! Lonely baronet whose wife has left him . . . in need of comfort. Little son dotes on you. What could be more promising? You'll be the second Lady Finch before we know where we are, *Santa Lucia*."

She trembled suddenly in her anger and despair.

"I've never heard such a lot of tripe, *really*."

"Forget it," he said. "I'm a bit overcome by the heat."

"I don't think I've made things any better for you by coming to this school," she said suddenly, fighting a dreadful desire to burst into tears. "But I'm going to leave. I'm going to hand in my notice. That may clear the air."

Now Nat gave her a long, direct look, which she could not begin to analyse except that she could sense a deep frustration and bitterness behind it which seemed incongruous with his flippancy.

"No need to do any such thing, Lucie," he said. "Keep your job if it appeals to you. *I'm* the one who's going to hand in my notice."

She gasped.

"You! You're going to leave Keynwood?"

"That is my present idea."

"But you can't!" she began. "Mr. Friern couldn't do without you. You're his right hand."

And she wanted to add:

'And neither can I do without you. Oh, Nat, please don't go!'

But no words came. She could only stand there helplessly, staring up at him, filled with forebodings.

20

"NOBODY is indispensable—so they say," Nat snapped back. "I may be the Head's right hand now but there is always a left hand, my dear."

Lucie began:

"Is it because—?" But Nat held up a warning hand.

"Don't ask for explanations, Lucie. As a rule I see things plainly, but just at the moment I feel right out of touch. Whatever my reasons for leaving Keynwood, they are not for publication."

Her lower lip trembled. Perhaps he saw it; perhaps that soft childish face of hers which had so much of sweetness, and of courage too, aroused his tenderness as it always used to do. Just for an instant he rested a hand on her shoulder.

"You're such a darling, Lucie. Don't let anything or anybody hurt you," he said.

At once she was filled with that suffocating sense of adoration and unfulfilled longing for him. It made her feel as though she were sinking . . . drowning . . . incapable of clear thought or action. In a choked voice she said:

"I don't know what you mean . . ."

"And I don't altogether know what I mean, either," he said with an abrupt laugh which held little humour, "except that I don't want *you* to be involved in this business."

"But I am—I *know* I am!" She summoned up the courage to cry those words aloud.

The man's dark restless eyes warned her.

"Don't be too sure, Lucie. I can only tell you that it's because *I'm* not sure about anything that I want to quit. And I beg you to believe that too many hazy conjectures and careless flinging around of one's emotions can prove dangerous."

"You're speaking in riddles!" she exclaimed.

"Perhaps I'd better not speak at all. I'll only say the wrong words and cause more confusion."

"Am I to lose your friendship, then, Nat?" she asked, in anguish.

"No," he said and narrowed his eyelids and then turned from her. "Not altogether. If you want me as a friend I'll try and be one to you, always."

"A thousand miles away, you mean!" she said with a strangled laugh. "You're going to the Colonies?"

"Not necessarily. Oh Lucie," he added, "you're such a child, a tactless, blundering little child, but quite adorable. I love you in my funny way. There—is that what you wanted me to say?"

"*Nat!*" She cried his name. Her heart seemed to turn over, looking up at him, her eyes grown dark and enormous behind the shielding glasses.

Something deep down in Nat Randall did indeed ache with a genuine love for her in this hour. He could easily have gathered her into his arms and put an end to all the stress and strain by telling her that there wasn't anybody else in the world except herself. But he could not. The shadow of Barbara Friern fell across them both and it was a large enough, important enough shadow to obliterate little Lucie. To annihilate him too, he thought. If he wasn't careful, Barbie would succeed in forcing him to stay here and involve him so hopelessly with her father and Keynwood and the whole outfit that he would never be able to extricate himself.

Right now, he told himself, he did not wish to be drawn into the matrimonial mesh with either of these girls. But if there was any key to his heart whatsoever, Lucie had it in her small capable hands. The dream that lay behind her starry gaze was his dream, too; but he would not acknowledge it nor let himself be beguiled by her gentleness, the sweet promise of her understanding or her passionate loyalty.

He was too uncertain and too suspicious of any love that was meant to be *for ever*. That sort of enduring love was the only love that Lucie would understand.

"Oh, let's put an end to all this," he said in a low violent tone, turned and marched away, leaving Lucie standing there bewildered and shaken. At the same moment Joanna Parrish suddenly appeared and walked up to Lucie.

"Hello, Matron—are you all right? You look as though you've seen a ghost."

Lucie pulled herself together and gave a shaky laugh.

"I don't think I've actually seen one but I do feel like a ghost. My . . . my head aches frightfully."

"It's been a tough day for you," said the Music mistress in her sympathetic way. "You've been run off your feet. I've watched you dashing around. Can I give you one of my Aspros and fetch you a glass of water?"

"No, no thanks. I'm going in now," said Lucie under her breath, and she turned and fled, in case Joanna should question her further.

Miss Parrish looked thoughtfully after the young figure in the white overall. She had seen rather more than Lucie knew. Nat Randall, talking to the little matron in what was palpably an intimate way. She had watched him stride off, later on, and leave Lucie alone. And she had thought:

'So that's it! Nat up to his old tricks. What a wretch he is!'

Joanna, alone of the women at Keynwood, had remained impervious to Nat's charm. She thought she knew him for what he was—just a gay philanderer with women. A cruel egotist. On the one occasion when he had tried to flirt with her in a mild way, she had snubbed him. She could remember the moment as though it were yesterday.

"Go try your fascination on somebody who will fall for it. I can see through you," she had said.

He hadn't been angry. He had given a low mocking laugh and answered:

"I didn't know I was so transparent. I must change my methods. How sad to feel you and I can never be friends. I was going to ask you to teach me to play the harp. It might have had an angelic influence on me."

Still laughing, he had strolled away from her. That had been in the Easter term, a year ago. Since then he had always smiled and nodded when they met, but nothing more. And, strangely enough, Joanna had gradually grown to regret 'putting him in his place' which, at the time, she had thought advisable. Without speaking to him at all she had never been quite unconscious of his extraordinary attraction when they did come in contact. What had happened between him and Lucie Reed? Joanna Parrish was suddenly filled with curiosity and then another emotion, foreign to her—envy. Her life at the moment was lonely and frustrated. Perhaps, she thought, Nat was only flirting with Lucie in his gay surface fashion. But it must mean something to have him stand there and look down at you the way he had done just now as he looked at Lucie! Then Joanna's envious reflections changed to contempt.

'He's a devil and Lucie's a little fool,' she reflected. 'I'm glad I've kept out of his way.'

Supper that evening was sheer torture for Lucie. Geoffrey Mallow had gone out. Only the Frierns and Nat were there. Barbara looked like a thundercloud. The two men kept up a steady flow of talk about the school and the events of the day. Lucie sat in complete silence, stricken, first of all, by the awful knowledge that Nat meant to go away, and secondly by the memory of those quite inexplicable words:

'*I love you.*'

Yes, he had actually said that. Undeniable fact.

He loved her . . . in what he called his 'funny way'. But that wasn't how she had wanted him to love her. She was posititive now that what he felt was only the friendly affectionate regard of a man toward a young girl whom he regarded as a child to whom one must be tolerant. But Lucie was all woman, torn with her passionate love for this man, and that declaration of love seemed to have made everything worse in her mind. She had come to Keynwood to 'get him' and all that had happened was that she had driven him away. She, or Barbara—or both of them.

She barely ate a thing but sat with her gaze lowered, looking at nobody, listening in bitter silence to the other voices. Nobody paid her any attention and she wondered whether Nat even cast a look in her direction.

'I can't bear it,' she thought. 'It's quite frightful!'

Once she dragged her gaze to Barbie's face. Looking at it . . . at the sulky red mouth that was so thin, so hard despite its sensuality . . . and at that glorious red hair which attracted Nat . . . she positively hated Barbara. Yet in a queer perverse way she wished that she could speak to her; confide in her. She conceived the ludicrous situation in which the two of them, who were in love with Nat, talked frankly to each other . . . exchanged notes . . . gave each other advice.

'I'm crazy tonight,' Lucie thought, 'I really am.'

Mrs. Friern pulled her out of the welter of her feelings back into the prosaic world in which she really existed in the school.

"Did you think that little Finch was a bit feverish tonight? Did you take his temperature, Matron?"

Glad to be drawn out of herself, Lucie replied:

"No, I didn't, Mrs. Friern. He wasn't the least bit feverish when he went to bed. He was merely over-excited."

Stella Friern, after a successful Fathers' Day, was inclined to be less censorious of her staff than usual. Graciously, she condescended to smile at Lucie.

"Oh, well . . . everything went off beautifully. Finch can be proud of his father, too. Sir Mark plays quite first-class cricket."

Mr. Friern caught these words and looked across the table at his wife.

"I absolutely agree, my dear. As a matter of fact, Mallow and I only learned today that Finch was a county cricketer in his youth."

"Such a distinguished-looking man. And such a pity that he married that dreadful woman," said Mrs. Friern, helping herself generously to cherry pie.

Lucie had been staring at her plate. But now she heard Nat's voice.

"Has Matron told you? Our handsome baronet has invited her to go with young Finch one day to see the ancestral home."

"No, really?" exclaimed Stella Friern.

Here, Barbara intervened:

"Well, *well*. Don't tell me Sir Mark has cast an eye in Matron's direction!"

The Headmaster laughed good-naturedly.

"And why not?"

Lucie sat tongue-tied, feeling her face and throat go hot and crimson. She wished desperately that they would all stop talking at her and about her. This thing was too ridiculous. But now Nat spoke again.

"I think she should go, and then tell us all about it. I rather envy her riding in that Rolls. It looks a peach of a car."

"Nothing is fixed, surely," said Mrs. Friern, on a warning note, "I haven't been told about any such outing."

Suddenly Lucie pushed her plate away, got up and said in a suffocated voice:

"I haven't the slightest intention of going to Sir Mark

Finch's house and I don't know what you're all talking about . . ."

Before anybody could speak again she had left the dining-room and shut the door behind her. Those who were left exchanged glances. Barbara gave a contemptuous laugh.

"*Temper!* Gracious! I didn't know Miss Reed was so lacking in a sense of humour."

"Oh, come, come, Barbie, maybe she was embarrassed. She didn't like having her leg pulled," said Mr. Friern with kindness.

"Personally," said Mrs. Friern, "I don't think it would be at all a good plan for her to go. Sir Mark hasn't even got his divorce yet."

"Isn't it all getting a bit out of proportion?" suggested Nat, "the poor girl only had an invitation to tea, and *with* young Finch. I would hardly think Sir Mark's divorce comes into it."

"Of course not. He wouldn't look twice at such an ordinary little thing," said Barbara acidly.

This was where Nat turned and looked long and hard at the girl at his side. He saw suddenly and with rather painful insight what a mean soul this girl possessed and how, despite all her looks and the rest that she might have to offer, a man might grow to detest that mean streak in her. He had been conscious, too, of regret when Lucie had rushed out of the room and of an amount of guilt. 'Ganging up' against little Lucie wasn't his idea of fun. She was too vulnerable. It wasn't even fair.

Deliberately he said:

"I don't know you're altogether right, Barbie. Matron isn't a glamour-girl but there's something very sweet about her."

"Really, men do see all kinds of things in women that their own sex can't distinguish," said Barbara, laughing.

The Headmaster, lighting his pipe, had been thinking about something entirely different, but now brought his thoughts back to Keynwood's matron. Without being in the least conscious of making a bad blunder in his daughter's estimation, he made what he had meant to be a humorous remark.

"Now, Nat. We all know what a lad you are. Men making passes at girls who wear glasses, eh?"

"Shame on you, Hugh," said Mrs. Friern indignantly.

The Headmaster gave his genial laugh. It was Barbara's turn to get up and walk away from the table. She turned in the doorway and flung a vicious remark over her shoulder:

"I don't think you've got the quotation quite right, Papa. I think girls with glasses are usually peeved because men *don't* make passes at them."

Mr. Friern changed the conversation. He was out of his depth in frivolous chatter of this kind. After his wife had left and he was alone with Nat, he turned to the subject of Keynwood's future.

"We're getting quite a few more letters every day. The requests for openings at Keynwood are on the increase and I'm having to turn more and more boys down. I think we may safely say that Keynwood will soon reach the level of Warnborough if things go on this way, Nat."

Nat was striving to sort out the tangle of his own dark and tortured mind. For a moment he maintained a gloomy silence while Hugh Friern continued to suggest that expansion was essential here. Then came the salient point. He needed a partner, he said.

He invited Nat to join him in the study for a smoke and a glass of port. (Hugh Friern preferred a good old-fashioned port to any other drink and it was the only one he had during the day.) Perforce, Nat followed him.

But not for long could he allow the Head to talk in circles around the subject of partnership, and Nat's value to the school. What Nat had told Lucie today held good. He wanted to leave and he believed that it was time he announced the fact.

Never in his life before had Nat Randall felt more in need of expanding his own life, his own ideas, and of finding a new *milieu*. If at times the memory of Lucie's large pain-filled eyes haunted and troubled him, he trod remorselessly on the vision. He said:

"I think it's as well that we talk about *my* future at Keynwood, Headmaster."

Mr. Friern smiled at the younger man.

" 'Hugh' . . . on these occasions, when we're alone together, eh?"

"Thanks, Hugh, and I think you know how much I value your friendship."

"And I yours, my dear boy. And, with these niceties over, let us come down to brass tacks," said Hugh with his happy, booming laugh. "Let us talk about you and a permanent niche at Keynwood."

But Nat had begun to pace the study with the restlessness of an animal in a cage. What he was about to say now would distress Hugh Friern. He knew it. He had a sincere admiration and affection for the Head of this school. The last thing he wanted to do was to upset him. But something had to be done about Barbara. The position had become too invidious.

'I've let it all go on too long,' Nat thought. 'Barbie . . . Lucie . . . all of them here will have the right to condemn me unless I pull myself together and attack this thing with honesty. It's time I indulged in a little emotional honesty . . . for the first time in my life.'

Mr. Friern looked at the slim, debonair figure of his 'right-hand' master. He took no notice of Nat's scowling face. He was used, after long years of working with him, to Nat's swiftly-changing moods.

"What's on your mind? Anything worrying you?" at length he asked.

"Plenty," said Nat.

"Well, if it's about your future, I think that what I'm going to say to you may help to resolve the situation. Keynwood's future is bound up not only with my activities as Headmaster and owner of the school, but with a man like yourself. You've been here for some time and made your mark. You get on well with the parents and you're a damned fine teacher. How would you like to come in as my partner, Nat—run the school *with* me, instead of under me?"

Nat had known this was coming. He felt hot and bothered. The summer night felt close and the study airless, despite the open window. Herta came in with two cups of coffee and left the tray on the desk. As she left, she cast a look at the handsome History master. Nat was used to the Danish girl's sidelong glances and sometimes, out of devilment, he returned them. But he was in no mood for any such nonsense. No mood for anything connected with women or flippancy, he thought. He knew what he had to do and he did it.

"You're not going to like what I'm going to say, Hugh," he rapped out, "but it must be done. You've just made me a very fine offer. I appreciate it from the bottom of my heart, and I'm more than flattered that you should even consider me as a partner. But I'm afraid I must turn it down, out of hand."

The bland, happy look left the older man's face.

"Good gracious, Nat. But why? Why, my dear fellow?"

"For a variety of reasons," muttered Nat. "It's all almost too complicated to enable me to explain."

"Oh come, my dear chap. Don't be timid. What about Barbara? Her mother and I are well aware that you and she—"

But here Nat broke in:

"Barbara is one of the difficulties, Hugh."

Mr. Friern's eyes brightened. He misunderstood. He slapped his thigh with one hand and laughed.

"Now, now, no need to feel any embarrassment. Stella and I know exactly how things are between you two."

Nat's pulse beats quickened. He mopped his forehead again as he came up to the Head's chair and stood directly in front of him.

"You're wrong, Hugh. You and Stella don't realise the truth."

"But we do. Come, Nat, let's put all our cards on the table."

"Yes, let us just do that thing," nodded Nat.

Mr. Friern spread out his fingers.

"Well? Barbie's devoted to you. More than that. She's in love with you. And that makes things a bit more simple, surely. If you and Barbie get married—what could be better? As my son-in-law, you immediately assume a more important position here. It will all be in the family, so to speak."

This time the little rivers of sweat ran down Nat's cheeks and he didn't bother to wipe them away. He said:

"What could be better indeed . . . *if* I were in love with Barbara."

Mr. Friern thrust his long legs in front of him, picked up his pipe and looked up at Nat with an expression of dismay.

"But *aren't* you?"

"No, I'm afraid I'm not," said Nat bluntly.

Hugh Friern went a bit pink about the gills. He stuttered:

"I . . . I am very sorry and . . . very surprised, I must say. Stella and I were convinced . . ." He paused, coughing.

"Yes, I know you were, and I'm to blame for letting it run on like this," said Nat. "I've seen far too much of

Barbara and naturally given rise to this sort of speculation. My only excuse is that we're thrown together rather a lot in a job like this."

"But she thinks that *you* . . ." began Mr. Friern.

"No, sir, she doesn't think so," Nat broke in again. "At least I've been honest with Barbie. She's always known that I have never counted myself a marrying man."

"But, my dear chap, you've got to get married and settle down one day. We all have. I mean those who want to forge ahead in our profession, and eventually obtain a Headmastership. Of course, some bachelors do very well indeed, but *I* think it's best for a Headmaster to have a wife at his side. Most helpful. Like Stella is to me. Don't you agree?"

"Yes. And if I'd cared in that way for Barbara it would have all been too easy."

Mr. Friern shook his head in a helpless way. He looked, Nat thought, ludicrously disappointed now.

"Have you told Barbie this?"

"More or less."

"But she still thinks . . . she said only last night . . . I know she expects . . ."

Nat interrupted these stammering statements.

"I intend to talk to Barbie as soon as possible and make her understand once and for all that it can't be . . . that I don't want to marry her."

"Oh dear!" said Hugh Friern, sadly. "Oh dear. What a blow!"

"I'm sorry, Hugh, and if you think I've behaved badly, you have every right to say so."

The Headmaster rubbed the back of his head.

"I don't think anything of the sort. Of course you two *have* seen a good deal of each other, I admit, but young people today seem to strike up these sort of friendships and then they come to nothing. But I think, all the same, that it's going to be a blow to Barbara."

"I'm truly sorry," said Nat under his breath. "I admire Barbie very much but I *don't* want to marry her."

"Is there someone else?" suddenly Mr. Friern asked him.

Ruthlessly, Nat stamped on the memory of that *other one.* "No."

Various ideas were forming in the Headmaster's mind but Lucie did not come into them. There was really nothing in

his mind or heart at the moment but a deep regret that Nat
was not to become his son-in-law. The young man had his
faults, nevertheless Hugh had always liked him immensely.
So did Stella. He was still further upset when Nat told him
now that he wished to give formal notice.

"But where will you go? What will you do? Could you
find a better school to work in?" asked Hugh Friern, a trifle
huffily.

"No better anywhere in the world, but I think I shall get
out of England."

Mr. Friern rose.

"Come, come, Nat, I am not going to take this too seriously.
I think it's just a mood that you will get over. So far as Barbie
is concerned she must face up to facts and you two must
just become good friends. But I don't want to lose you here.
No . . . no more arguments tonight . . . enough has been said.
I'm a great believer in sleeping on a thing like this. Why not
let it go for, say, a week? We'll talk again then and see how
you feel. If you like, I'll speak to Barbara."

"No—I've got to do my own dirty work," said Nat with
a faint smile. "Please don't say anything to her."

Hugh Friern gave the younger man a long, searching look
over his horn-rims.

"I've felt for some time that something has been un-
settling you, Nat, but these things pass. *Don't* do anything
in a rash moment. Remember that I need you here."

"You're being extraordinarily nice to me, sir, but I'm
afraid that I'm not going to change my mind."

It was on this note that Nat left the study. He saw Barbara
in the garden but avoided going anywhere near her. He did
not feel that he could stand another difficult personal discussion tonight. As for the future—he knew less in this hour,
he reflected grimly, about what he wanted or intended to do
than he had ever known. One thing alone was clear to him:
the need for honesty, even if it scalded.

The summer night was still light and beautiful. He went
round to the garage and started up his car. He needed to get
away from the school-house and be alone, in order to think.

Upstairs in their bedroom the Frierns discussed Nat.

"I'm shocked and angry. I think Nat's behaved disgrace-
fully to Barbie," announced Stella, hotly.

"My dear, that's a truly feminine outlook," said her husband.

"The chap has tried to be fair and tell the truth tonight. Don't let's condemn him for that."

"But he hasn't played fair with Barbie."

"I think that's a sweeping statement. They've been thrown together a great deal but he assures me that he has always warned her that he wasn't a marrying man."

But Stella, frowning, feeling a tigress in defence of her young, indulged in less tolerant reflections. She was beginning to wonder if some of the chance remarks she had heard from Barbara (and others) about Lucie Reed had any foundation. Was *she* carrying on with Mr. Randall? If so, she was a sly little thing and *she* was the one who was going to leave Keynwood. Not Nat.

"I shall talk to Master Nat tomorrow. I shall handle this thing," she announced.

"My dear," said the Headmaster, removing his glasses and blinking at his wife, "I beg you to do nothing of the kind."

"Then you can save your breath, Hugh, because I intend to do it," said Stella.

Mr. Friern shrugged his shoulders. He had enough trouble for one evening and he had no wish to argue with Stella in this mood. When she wanted to do a thing she did it, and nobody knew that better than himself. What was it he had said to Randall about a wife being a help? Stella on the warpath was no help to anybody; she usually made things worse.

Headmaster of Keynwood he was, he thought, sighing, and, he hoped, liked and respected by all and feared by none. A man whose word was law and who was a dictator in this small world which comprised his school. Strange, he reflected, as he settled down in his bed that night and took a look at his favourite book of Homer's *Iliad*, that in that other, matrimonial world, he had no control at all.

It was a relief to him when, in fact, Stella changed her mind and did not attack Nat, and Barbie received an invitation to stay in Geneva for a short time which she accepted.

21

T HAT next day, Lucie saw nothing of Nat except at dinner
      and odd glimpses which she caught of him in the school-
house or grounds . . . but never alone. So she suffered from
knowing nothing of what was going on and was put to the
fresh pain of believing that she might never be given another
chance to meet him outside Keynwood.

Something had happened to Barbara, of that Lucie was
convinced, because Miss Friern suddenly vanished. Stella
announced that her daughter had flown to Geneva on urgent
business and would be away for a week. During that week,
a Miss Johnson, a friend of Joanna Parrish, came in daily
from Horsham to undertake the secretarial work that Barbara
had been doing.

There was a time when Lucie would have been delighted
that her 'rival' had gone away. She guessed that Barbara had
found out that things were not as she wanted them where
Nat was concerned, and that she had run out on the school
and her parents in a fit of the sulks. It was mere conjecture
and brought Lucie no feeling of triumph because she, herself,
seemed to be getting no further with the much-loved man of
her heart. She had nothing to comfort her now but the
knowledge that he had once said, "I love you!" (even if it
wasn't in the way she wanted).

'I feel like Barbie,' Lucie thought, unhappily. 'I'd like to
have friends abroad to whom I could fly and get away from
this misery.'

In the week that followed Fathers' Day, Marta returned
from Malta. She wrote to her friend and asked her to telephone
her at the flat which Marta and Guy had taken in Eaton
Square. Lucie went out to the call-box and made the call.
After listening to Marta's ecstatic description of her honeymoon Lucie poured her own heart out. She told Marta everything that had happened.

Marta said:

"But you little *imbecile*. Don't give up *now*. How can you
be such a defeatist?"

"But I *am* defeated," said Lucie wildly. "He doesn't want to marry me or Barbie or anybody."

"I don't believe it. I think you've won the first trick. Barbara's been given her *congé* and she's pushed off, if only for a week. I know her type. Now that she's failed with Nat she'll be perfectly beastly once she gets back and they won't have a nice word to say to each other."

"That won't help me. Anyhow, Nat himself is determined to leave Keynwood."

"Who cares? What is more important is that he should leave with, and not without, you."

"Oh, Marta!" Lucie choked over the name. It was suffocatingly hot in the telephone kiosk. She drew the back of one hand wearily across her damp forehead. "I'll never, never make the grade. He doesn't love me that way."

"I've a hunch that he might if you don't give in now," said Marta.

"Oh, Marta, I'm not like you. I haven't got your courage or determination."

"Oh, yes you have—and I'll be very cross with you if you don't show your mettle. I think—and my hunches are usually right—that Nat's in love with you in just the way you want, only he can't bring himself to say so."

"Any more of this 'go get your man' business and he'll fade out of my life even as a friend," said Lucie bitterly.

"Nonsense. You just carry on as though nothing has happened and act the sweet, adoring, comforting little thing. That's how he likes you," giggled Marta.

Lucie felt a good deal better and began to laugh and talk more normally with her friend. But she was still depressed when she returned to the school.

One of the things that Marta had advised her to do was to try and make Nat aware of her as a woman by seeing her through the eyes of another man. In other words, by making him jealous. Why couldn't she start an affair with Geoffrey Mallow? Marta had asked. But that was a thing Lucie couldn't do. She wasn't unscrupulous enough. Geoffrey had made it quite plain that he was more than a little fond of her. The last thing she meant to do was to encourage *him*. She had suffered too much herself; she wasn't going to raise false hopes in any man.

But she made up her mind suddenly to accept Mark Finch's

invitation. Remembering how they had all teased her, she decided to show them that she *wasn't* the timid left-out-in-the-cold little Lucie they imagined. It might give Nat something to think about, too. So when the expected invitation actually came from Sir Mark, Lucie went to Stella Friern and asked permission to accept.

"By all means go out to tea with the Finch boy and his father, and I hope you enjoy it," was Stella's somewhat sour reply.

When the gleaming Rolls pulled up at Keynwood that following Sunday, Nat happened to be there by the front doorway. He saw Lucie, hand in hand with an excited small boy, dressed up for her 'date'. He had to admit she looked charming in a royal-blue dress and jacket with a deep white collar, and a little white sailor hat. She was not wearing her glasses. She was looking prettier than he ever remembered her.

"My, my!" he murmured, as she passed him.

Her cheeks went pink, her lashes drooped. Then: "I'm going to have a *wonderful* time," she said, lifting her head and staring him full in the eyes.

"You're looking wonderful," he smiled.

Her colour deepened. Young Finch was chatting to his father's chauffeur. Lucie lingered a moment beside Nat.

"How's life?" she asked lightly. "I haven't seen you to talk to lately."

He had no intention of telling her what his life was like. It was far too complicated. The scene he had had with Barbie before she left the school had been far from happy, and there was a certain amount of tension now between himself and the Headmaster—to say nothing of frowning coldness from Stella. None of it was making life any easier. He knew that Barbie had rushed over to her friend in Geneva in order to show her fury, and her loathing of him because he had turned her down; but she had to return next week and from then until the end of term there was bound to be a tricky situation here. Hugh made things worse by refusing to accept Nat's notice and insisting that he should come back to Keynwood, if only for one more term.

Now Nat looked at Lucie; so charming, so youthful, in her pretty summer dress, her short white cotton gloves and blue and white shoes. He wished, gloomily, that things could be different. That he could free himself from all the inhibitions that kept him away from Lucie—and love. Yet, he reflected, she was as fragrant and sweet as one of the roses in this garden, and from her sweetness a man could draw the same delight that a thirsty wanderer in the desert would draw from a suddenly discovered well of cool, clear water.

He was beginning to feel that he regretted the whole of his life. He said:

"I've wanted to talk to you, Lucie. Please believe me when I say that, but I think I'd better keep away from you."

"But why—?" she began, under her breath, dismay widening her eyes. He stood aside, suddenly whispering:

"Get along, dear. I see Stella."

"Then promise that you *will* talk to me, sometime."

"I promise," he said.

The chauffeur opened the door of the Rolls. The matron and little Finch stepped into it. Nat watched the car out of sight. He wished suddenly that he was Mark Finch waiting at the other end to receive Lucie; without anything in his mind but the happy, uninhibited wish to entertain her, and knowing that he would soon be free to ask her to share the rest of his life—if he ever felt that way about her.

'I've made a mess of *my* life—I can't see the wood for the trees,' Nat reflected, in the bitterness of his mood. 'It will be best for me to say good-bye to Lucie and stick to it this time—and never see her again once I leave Keynwood.'

22

THE Frierns were out to dinner that night. The Head had taken his wife to Worthing to see an old aunt who had just gone down there to live.

Nat, Geoff Mallow, Berry and Lucie were alone for the evening meal. The young matron somewhat surprised the other three. She was far less subdued than usual. She talked incessantly, with very pink cheeks and bright eyes and chin tilted, as though defying them all to deny that she had had a wonderful time and was a most privileged person.

Miss Day had started the ball rolling by asking Lucie how she got on at Sir Mark Finch's home. Geoff had seconded the question.

"Yes, tell us all, Matron. We didn't expect you in tonight. Isn't it your evening off?"

"Yes, I should have stayed out, only my sister and her husband went to the Brighton Hippodrome and as it started to rain just before I left Sir Mark's place I decided to come straight here."

Nat said nothing and asked no questions. He sat staring moodily at his plate and shook his head at most of the things that Herta offered. He seemed to have a poor appetite and to be indulging in a black reverie. He was, of course, conscious of that pink challenging young face on the other side of the table and heard every word of the gay, enthusiastic description of the tea-party with young Finch and his father. She was 'shooting a line', he thought; none of it sounded at all like Lucie. What message she was intending to convey to *him*, if any, he didn't quite know. But she certainly harped on the name of Mark Finch. How delightful he was; what marvellous manners he had; what a wonderful house, full of antiques and beautiful paintings.

"They have an original Turner—just think of it! A wonderful golden painting of the Thames. It must be worth thousands. And a painting of Sir Mark's mother by the famous Cowan Dobson. Everything there is in such perfect taste. I seemed to be living in another world."

Here Beryl Day interrupted the girlish voice with one of her shrill laughs.

"Didn't you miss the perfect taste and all the originals here at Keynwood?"

"Now, Berry—let the child continue," said Geoffrey.

"Child indeed!" said Lucie, indignantly.

"That's all you are, really," he said.

His nice friendly gaze met hers across the table. She smiled back. Geoffrey always flattered her. Berry had often told her that she was the first and only resident 'female' to whom Geoff had ever paid the slightest attention. It was true, also, that Mark Finch had been marvellous to her, and made her feel a family friend rather than an obscure little matron from a boys' school. After he had taken her over the house and the butler had served tea, little Finch had caused some embarrassment by clutching Lucie's arm and saying to his father:

"I wish we didn't have to go back to school and that Matron could live here with us, Dad."

Mark Finch had laughed and caught Lucie's eye.

"I'm not sure I don't wish that myself, old boy," he had said.

Of course it had been nonsense. But enough to make Lucie feel that perhaps she had underestimated herself and that men *did* find her attractive. Queer that she had never thought so, in the past, and used to protest when Marta told her so. But Mark Finch had, certainly, shewn her every possible attention and made it clear that he had not only welcomed her to Jeremy's home today but hoped that she would repeat the outing. Yet in the Rolls, driving back to Keynwood, with little Finch chatting like a magpie beside her, it was not of Sir Mark she had thought, but Nat. *It was always Nat.* She was so afraid that it would always be like this. As for Marta telling her to carry on with the 'battle', she had almost—yes *almost*—reached the stage where she considered it hopeless.

All through the meal tonight she was miserably conscious of Nat's silence and depression. Toward the end he put in a slightly embittered remark.

"These chaps like Finch seem to have everything. It must be pleasant, even in these days of crippling taxation, to be able to spend what's left of the family fortune and attend to a few directorships without having to do too much work."

"Get away!" protested Berry. "You love your work, Nat. Always got your head in a book, and you're a born teacher."

"And don't forget," suddenly Lucie put in, looking at Nat, "that a man like Sir Mark hasn't got everything. Possibly he loved his wife and it must be wretched for him having to divorce her, especially as she is Jeremy's mother."

"Our dear, sentimental, soft-hearted little matron," said Geoffrey, with a laugh.

Lucie crimsoned and tilted her chin a bit higher.

"Well, it's true, isn't it?"

"It might be," said Nat coldly. "It also might be equally true that Finch is delighted to be getting rid of his wife."

"There speaks our cynical, angry young man," giggled Berry, grimacing at Nat. "*Ever* so unromantic, aren't we, dear?"

He rose, hunching his shoulders in a way that Lucie knew well—meaning that he was trying to justify a remark he didn't really believe in. He lit the inevitable cigarette.

"Anyhow, our matron has had a lovely time with the noble baronet, and that's what the tea-party was in aid of," he drawled, and walked out of the room.

Lucie's heart beat fast. All her enthusiasm and gaiety evaporated. She felt like a pricked balloon.

Berry tucked an evening paper under her arm and made for the door.

"I've got some exam papers to work on. Be seeing you, Lucie."

Lucie thought:

'Good old "Horsey"—always equable. No muddled emotions. Full of her teaching and her pupils. Like Joanna Parrish, with her music. I rather envy them their singleness of purpose. I seem to be drifting around and all I do is sink in a swamp that nobody has warned me about. Or perhaps it is that even if I am warned I still go ahead and deliberately get myself bogged.'

"Come for a stroll after coffee, Matron?" suggested Geoffrey.

"Love to," said Lucie.

They took the walk through the Headmaster's garden which was lovely even on this grey, sunless evening. The rain had stopped. It was damp underfoot, even cold. The tall blue heads of the delphiniums were sodden and heavy, and drooping sadly. Lucie watched Geoffrey tie them up to their stakes with the tender hand of the real gardener.

"Not a good beginning for July," he said. "This may be the start of the long wet spell they talk about, which means we've had our summer. I've decided to give up delphiniums, Lucie, and raise some really good zinnias next year. Incidentally, what are your favourite flowers?"

It was 'Lucie' when they were alone, and 'Matron' in the school-house. She tried to drag her mind from Nat and talk to Geoffrey.

"Lilies-of-the-valley," she said promptly.

Geoffrey stood up and wiped the raindrops from his fingers. "*Convallaria Magalia*, and very lovely too."

"You and your Latin names!" murmured Lucie, smiling.

"I might try a bed of them specially for you," he said. "We

could put in the *Fortins Giant*—they're extra large. Want nice, light well-drained soil. It may be a bit too heavy here but I can get hold of some compost and start them off under cloches . . ."

He continued to tell her about the cultivation of the lilies, and ended by saying that by next May or June he would have a show for her.

Then suddenly Lucie said:

"But, Geoffrey, I don't think I shall be here."

Silence a moment. If the man was conscious of very real regret—and surprise—he tried not to show it. He had never been one to show his feelings easily. But he was certainly disappointed. He said:

"Don't tell me you're going to chuck your job? Aren't you happy here?"

"No, I'm not," she said bluntly.

"Oh, dear," said Geoffrey, with a simple regret that warmed her heart.

She went on:

"I love the school, Geoff. It's a . . . a *personal* thing."

He stood biting his lip and fumbled in his coat-pocket for a much-needed pipe. He thought he was beginning to see daylight about the little matron.

He knew that a love affair was the cause of her unhappiness. And once or twice he had suspected that it was Nat Randall. Tonight he was sure of it. He felt a sudden anger against Nat Randall. The chap was a supreme egotist. Surely no fellow worth his salt would want to make this nice child unhappy.

Indignation took the customary guard off Geoffrey's tongue. He said:

"Look here, Lucie. I'm fond of you and I'm going to speak my mind. It's Randall—isn't it?"

She caught her breath and turned away, cheeks and throat burning, then paling again.

"I didn't think anybody knew," she whispered.

"Well, I don't know about other people but I've guessed for a long time."

"I suppose you think I'm crazy."

"No," said Geoffrey sadly, "I only think that Randall can't realise how honoured and lucky he is and I rather wish I was in his place, that's all."

"Oh!" said Lucie in a choked voice and put the back of her hand against her lips.

"It's all right, my dear. That's the way things go. A loves B and B loves C—and so on. Go on looking upon me as Big Brother. That's the name you once gave me and the name I'd like to keep."

She swung round to him and put out a hand and as he caught and held it, she said:

"You're really the nicest man in the world, Geoffrey."

"But it all adds up to the fact that you're fond of Nat Randall," he said wryly.

"It all began a year ago. I'm afraid I never quite got Nat out of my system."

"Perhaps it wasn't very wise of you to come to Keynwood, Lucie."

"I'm sure it was very *unwise*," she agreed, with a bitter little laugh.

"And you know for a positive fact that he doesn't return your feelings?"

"I think I know it for a fact," she said, and her head drooped so that he couldn't see the swift tears that stung her eyelids.

Geoffrey stared at the delphiniums. He felt a sharp pain of grief for her and because of her. He did not quite know what to say. But the awkward moment was put to an end by the short unattractive figure of Miss Day running across the damp lawn toward them, waving her arms, excitedly.

They both turned and walked back to the school-house. Berry met them, her face red, her bosom heaving.

"I say, you two, we've just had awful news."

"What sort of news?" asked Geoffrey.

"About the Head."

"The Head?" Geoffrey and Lucie echoed the name in unison.

Berry, panting, nodded. The news she gave them was certainly not good. Just now, she said, while she was working on some papers in the common-room, Nat had rushed in to tell her that he had had a telephone call from a doctor's house near Cowfold. It appeared that Hugh and Stella Friern, returning from Worthing, had been virtually pushed off the road by a car that had skidded. The Frierns' car had crashed into a tree. Stella Friern (who was the one who had telephoned) seemed to be miraculously unhurt—merely shaken. But Hugh Friern's face and forehead had been cut and his nose damaged.

He was not *too* bad, Berry reassured Lucie and Geoffrey, as they looked at her with horror—nothing else the matter. He had been taken to the nearest hospital to be stitched up. Nat had just gone off to fetch Stella. It was possible, they thought, that Hugh's nose was broken. They would, of course, X-ray him at once.

"He'll certainly be out of action for the next week, even if they let him come home tomorrow," Berry ended her dismal story. "Isn't it rotten luck—just the last two weeks of term?"

"Absolutely grim," said Geoffrey.

"Oh, dear, these ghastly roads and smashes," said Lucie, feeling slightly sick.

As the three of them entered the common-room to discuss the accident, Lucie added that she thought she had better go and get a bed ready for Stella. Even if she was able to come home, she would need a little nursing. She would be in a state of shock.

"I reckon," said Berry, "that they'll keep the Head in hospital. It might be the best thing. Nat will have to take over here."

"But he's quite good at that," said Geoffrey generously. "Randall's first-class in an emergency. He did excellent work when the Head was ill a year or two ago."

"And do you know," put in Berry, lowering her voice, "there's a strong rumour that Nat is leaving Keynwood next term. Mrs. Friern as good as hinted it to me."

Geoffrey glanced at Lucie. He saw a stricken look in her eyes and realised that things were rather worse with these two than he had thought. No good both of them quitting the school, he thought crossly. He hated changes of staff and he particularly disliked the thought of losing the new matron.

After that, there was no more time for conversation or wild conjecture. Nat would soon be back with Stella Friern. And thinking of what Lucie had said about the state of the roads today, the Frierns were lucky, Geoffrey thought grimly, to have got off so lightly.

23

Deep gloom hung over Keynwood.

Hugh Friern was not allowed to come home from the hospital. They wished to keep him there for a few days. Stella returned alone. Being a woman of spirit, she clung tenaciously to her usual routine of work and assured everybody that she was none the worse for the crash although it was obvious that her nerves were shaken. Nat, being next in seniority, automatically stepped into the Headmaster's place and took the brunt of the work upon his shoulders. The redoubtable Stella earned Lucie's regard, not only because of her physical courage but by the way in which she, as well as Nat, took on the Headmaster's responsibilities. Stella had taken a degree in Maths and been a Maths mistress in a girls' school when Hugh first met her. Bravely now she tackled the problem of Hugh's classes at Keynwood.

On Lucie's shoulders, therefore, fell the full burden of a matron's duties without the usual help or guidance from Mrs. Friern. But some degree of warmth and understanding was established between the two women following upon that car-smash. Not only did Lucie's respect for the rather difficult Stella increase but Stella, herself, saw quite a few new qualities in Miss Reed. She was never to forget the young matron's kindness on the night that Nat brought her home from Cowfold.

Lucie had the bed warmed, and was ready with hot milk and brandy. Without fussing Stella, she induced her to go straight to bed and stay quiet and with the help of some tablets, sleep off the effects of the crash.

"It wasn't Hugh's fault . . ." Stella kept saying.

"We're all quite sure it wasn't, Mrs. Friern," Lucie replied. "We all know what a safe driver the Head is. The other car must have been going too fast. We must just thank God that Mr. Friern has nothing more than a broken nose and bruises."

Stella sighed deeply. She was in bed, sipping her hot milk when this conversation took place.

"I'm afraid my husband will break his heart at having to

miss even a week of the term—especially when exams are so soon beginning," she said regretfully.

"Please try not to worry. I'll do everything I can to help as far as my own job is concerned," Lucie assured her.

And that was when Stella looked at the earnest young face of her matron and thought:

'She's really a sweet little thing. I think Barbie's been wrong about her. But Barbie takes these dislikes . . .'

Barbie's return from Geneva that very next day did not help the atmosphere at Keynwood. As soon as she got home she created tension and unpleasantness. She rushed to the hospital to see her father and exhibited a fine show of anxiety but was of little real help to anybody, because she was still so tied up with her own affairs. She was angry and resentful at having been 'turned down' by Nat Randall. She avoided him, exchanged only a few necessary words with him in public, and ignored Lucie. The younger girl accepted this but gave no outward sign that Miss Friern's attitude upset her. Lucie was, in fact, too busy with her boys. In spite of Nat's cool efficiency as controller of the school, a certain amount of disorganisation was caused because of the Head's absence.

There came a touching moment when the boys found out exactly when their Headmaster was due back from hospital. They hid in the bushes by the lodge at the gate. As Nat's car turned in (he had gone to fetch Mr. Friern home) the entire school darted out waving flags which had not been unearthed since the Coronation. They brought the car to a standstill while they swarmed around, cheering and whistling.

They then followed the slow-moving car to the front door over which they had placed a large piece of white cardboard bearing the badly-printed words:

WELCOME HOME TO OUR HEAD

Hugh Friern stepped out, hiding his emotion and pleasure as best he could. His head and nose were bandaged. He leaned on Nat's arm. He was suffering from delayed shock and realised that it would be at least a week or ten days before he could resume work in the school. But he waved cheerfully at the boys, as Nat held up a hand for silence. He said:

"Thanks, boys. Thank you a very great deal for your kind reception. All I can say is we must be thankful that things weren't worse. Sorry I've come back looking like 'The Invisible Man'. God bless you all."

The boys laughed, and cheered him again.

Lucie, who had been 'briefed' by young Olifant about the plans for this reception, witnessed it and herself felt close to tears. Little devils these boys might be at times, but they had warm hearts and the way they greeted the Headmaster was, she thought, a sign of the affection they bore him.

She met Nat in the hall after he and Stella had helped Hugh Friern up to his bedroom. It was the first time for several days she had seen Nat to speak to alone. He looked, she thought, rather haggard and tired. He returned her gaze, unsmiling.

"You must be thankful to have the Head home," Lucie said, breaking the awkward silence.

"Yes. It's good to feel authority is back where it belongs, although of course I'll have to go on acting for him. Incidentally, he said on the way here that he doesn't want anything cancelled and he doesn't want a 'hush' in the house, so to speak, as though he were a sick man. Let things run their normal course. The sound of the boys' voices will help him to get better all the quicker."

"Nat," said Lucie, coming suddenly nearer him, with her pulse-rate quickening, "I want to tell you there's a rumour right through the school that you're leaving Keynwood."

"News is quick to get round," he said stiffly.

"Then you really mean to go?" she asked under her breath.

"If not this term—at Christmas, yes. The Head's so cut up about my leaving that I may have to stay on another term. I don't want to walk out on him cold. He's been so decent to me."

"I see," said Lucie. "Then don't worry about me . . . I mean . . . I know I've caused a certain amount of nuisance . . . I mean . . . *I'll* give notice. I won't come back after the summer holidays."

"Oh, for God's sake, Lucie," Nat said with sudden passion, "I don't want to upset your life and plans any more than you want to upset mine. Stella Friern's been singing your praises these last few days. You seem to have got into her good books. They all love you here. Do please be sensible. Stay on."

She looked up at him, a little bewildered by his vehemence.

"But you can't want me to stay if *you're* still going to be here," she began.

"Who said I didn't want you—?" he began—words that made more mark on her than the sight of his scowl. He went on: "Lucie, I'd like to have an hour alone with you— one of our talks—but with me in the Headmaster's place it's even more impossible than usual. I just can't get out to meet you."

"Do you want to, Nat?" she asked, wistfully.

He gave a brief laugh.

"Just at the moment I'm not sure what I want, Lucie. There are moments when I think it would be best if we never set eyes on each other again. And other moments when I feel I can never do what I did a year ago, and just chuck you out of my life."

She looked at him speechlessly. Quickly he continued:

"Of course, the time will come when I *can* tactfully ask you to meet me again, but by then you may be too busy in the Rolls with your baronet."

Another joyful leap of her heart. Could she detect a jealous note mixed up with the asperity of that remark, she wondered.

Now she did what she was certain Marta would have told her to do. She laughed.

"Any girl would find it hard to say 'no' to a 'Silver Cloud'. That's the name of Sir Mark's car, so he told me."

Nat emerged from the welter and conflict of his deepest thoughts and seemed suddenly to see a new and tantalising Lucie. She was not quite the meek, slavish little thing, waiting for him to distribute favours, that he had thought her in the past. Suddenly, furiously annoyed by the thought of Mark Finch, his 'Silver Cloud', and his interest in Lucie, Nat turned, marched into the Headmaster's study and shut the door rather noisily.

But Lucie's heart was singing. That abrupt withdrawal did not depress her. She stood looking at the closed door with tender, thoughtful gaze, and a renewal of wild hope in her heart.

She was on her way upstairs after giving the junior boys their tea, when she met Barbara Friern coming out of her own bedroom. Barbara had barely exchanged more than a formal 'good-morning' or 'good-night' with the matron since her return from abroad. Her handsome face had a pinched, thin look about it that made Lucie feel almost sorry for her.

"Oh, by the way, Matron," she snapped, "I'd like a word with you in my room if you don't mind."

"Of course," said Lucie, but as she followed the other girl into that blue and white room she felt faintly nervous. What was coming now? Irresistibly her gaze was drawn to the mantelpiece. The photograph of Nat was no longer there. He had been dethroned, Lucie thought wryly.

Barbara said:

"Sit down, please."

Lucie seated herself.

Barbara stood facing her. Her cold blue eyes examined Lucie as though she were an extraordinary phenomenon. Then she said:

"Can it be possible that Nat Randall is really interested in *you*?"

If she had thrown a bomb at Lucie's feet, the younger girl could not have felt more shocked.

"Why, Barbie—" she began to protest.

Barbara cut in:

"Don't let's beat around the bush. Let's behave like sensible thinking women instead of two hysterical females fighting over a bone."

"I don't know what you mean!" Lucie stuttered.

"Yes, you do. Nat is the bone. I saw you look straight at my mantelpiece. You thought Nat's photo was going to be there, didn't you?"

"Okay—since you're so discerning," said Lucie, setting her teeth, and there followed the reflection: 'Barbie wants an open fight. It'll be too ghastly! I shan't know what to say.'

And she didn't know what to say when Barbie began to walk up and down the bedroom, hands thrust in the pockets of the full skirt she was wearing with a sweater, and calmly, coldly, analysed the whole situation.

"Everything was all right for me until you came to Keynwood. Nat was in love with me. I know it. Everybody knew that he was going to be offered a partnership with my father and I had it all nicely planned. Then *you* had to come."

"But look here—" began Lucie.

"No, wait," broke in Barbara, "I'll have my say if I die for it. You came to Keynwood under false pretences, anyhow."

Lucie sprang to her feet.

"I deny that."

"You can't. None of us was aware that you were on such intimate terms with Nat Randall when we accepted you here as matron."

Scarlet to the roots of her hair, Lucie stood looking at her adversary. Her heart beat unpleasantly fast.

"It isn't true that Nat and I were *ever* on intimate terms."

"But you had some sort of an affair," Barbara accused her, "then you came here to chase after him. I can see it all now. It's even possible that Nat's been playing a double game and that he originally got you here to amuse him, even while he was making love to me. Yes. *Making love to me*," she repeated violently.

Lucie gasped. This was more than she had bargained for. She felt sick with shame for Barbara . . . and the old jealousy sprang up. But there was a spirited determination in her not to be beaten by this unpleasant girl. Any pity that she might have had for Barbara, because she thought she had lost Nat, vanished.

"You're saying some very horrible things which are quite untrue," declared Lucie. "First of all, Nat had no idea I was taking the job, and he has never 'amused himself', as you call it, with me. Secondly, although I admit that I have always been fond of Nat, we had *no* firm understanding. As for you, I had no idea whatsoever that there was anything at *all* between you and him—at least, not until I arrived at Keynwood."

"So you admit you knew it once you got here?"

"It became obvious to me that you liked Nat, yes."

Barbara stopped and faced Lucie, an ugly look in her eyes.

"How dare you put it that way! The 'liking' wasn't all on my part. He wanted me until you came and spoiled things."

"If that is so, I'm sorry," said Lucie quietly, "but if Nat had really been in love with you, my coming would have made no difference to you both. If he had wanted to marry you, Barbara, nobody on earth could have got him away from you. I know him well enough for that."

"So you insist that he didn't want to marry me," said Barbara between her teeth.

"I'd rather not carry on with this discussion. It's horrible, and it won't do any good. You're behaving as though I've taken Nat away from you. Well, I haven't. Anyhow, he doesn't belong to *me* any more than he does to *you*. He doesn't belong to anybody but himself."

Silence. A look of doubt had crossed Barbara's passionate face. Then she said in a low voice:

"If I thought that was true . . ." She broke off, then spoke to Lucie on a less offensive note: "Look here, maybe I've said more than I should have done and I'm sorry if I've upset you. But this happens to mean the hell of a lot to me."

Lucie made no reply. Barbara continued:

"I had everything in the world to give Nat, and his heart is really here at Keynwood. Why don't *you* go away and give him a chance—give *me* a chance, too. He may find you attractive. I don't deny it. I suppose you have some peculiar charm for him . . ." She shrugged her shoulders, as though wishful to imply that she didn't understand it. "But there's a lot in propinquity and if you were not here Nat would get closer to me again. You can't further his career as I can. Don't you realise that? You'll ruin him. If you were really fond of him, you'd go away at the end of this term."

As Lucie still remained silent, Barbara tried to further her case.

"Do you want to be obstinate and wreck Nat. *Do you?*"

Lucie all this time was struggling in her mind to digest the things that had been so shamelessly and forcibly said. Could it be possible that Barbie was right? she asked herself in dismay. Would it really be best for Nat and his future for him to stay at Keynwood and was it true that her coming here had 'wrecked him'? Had she destroyed everybody's peace? And if she went away again, *would* Nat go back to Barbara? *Did he want to go back?* He had said that he did not wish to be involved with any woman. Was that strictly true? If only she knew!

24

SHE asked Barbara a question, suddenly, almost passionately. "Do you *really* feel that Nat would turn to you if I—faded out?"

Barbara's lashes flickered. She was trying to convince herself that this was so, against her own judgment. She could not really forget some of the blunt and even cruel things that

Nat had said to her when she made her last desperate effort to retain mastery of him.

She remembered those words now. He had said:

"Oscar Wilde, you will remember, wrote a few lines which indicated that the brave man kills love with a sword and the coward with a kiss. I've been a coward about you lately. It's out of date to suppose that a few kisses mean marriage, but one can carry things too far and I don't intend to act the coward any longer whether I lose your regard or your father's friendship or my job. I mean to be honest with you and with myself now. *I do not want to marry you, Barbara.*"

She had screamed at him then, bringing Lucie's name into the hysteria, but it had made no difference. But now she didn't care whether he meant to marry her or not. She only knew that she would not have the humiliation of seeing him take Lucie in preference.

Deliberately she lied, without scruple, avoiding the candour and simplicity in the eyes of the little matron, looking so gravely at her through horn-rimmed glasses.

"I *know* that Nat would turn to me if you left," Barbara said. "I only ask you to give me a chance."

Lucie bit her lip. Somehow this was not in line with the way Nat generally spoke about Barbara, yet there was, she supposed, a degree of truth in her allegations. Lucie in coming here *had* caused something of a rift between the other two.

Suddenly she said:

"All right. I'll give you a sporting chance. It's up to Nat, too. I'll go away. I'll stay away. It's only another fortnight to the end of term. He's frightfully busy now in the Head's place. And I think we both know that he doesn't want to be involved at the moment in any kind of emotional affair. What he chooses to do in the holidays is his pigeon."

Barbara's heart leapt.

"He's coming back here, anyhow. My father has induced him to stay for at least one more term and I guarantee that if you're not here things will slip back to where they were before you came to Keynwood."

Lucie turned away. Having said all these things which were natural to her generous, tender heart, she had the hideous feeling that she was making a mistake. If Marta were here she would be horrified. Lucie could hear her saying:

'Don't be so cracked, you little defeatist. Don't let this Barbie female get your man. She's a nasty bit of work and she doesn't deserve him anyway. Go get him for yourself. This heroic self-sacrifice when you don't even know whether Nat wants it, is just absurd. Boer War stuff, let alone First World War! Don't be so old-fashioned. You came to Keynwood because you wanted Nat. Give up, and I'll never respect you again.'

That's what Marta would say. Lucie put both hands over her ears as though to shut out the warm vigorous voice of her friend, the friend who had got what she wanted out of life and was now so utterly content.

Barbie said:

"Well, thanks a lot. I suppose I must admit that you're being very co-operative, my dear Matron."

Perhaps it was the way in which she drawled those words. Perhaps the latent sneer behind her method of address. 'My dear Matron' indeed! That cold baleful blue eye and thin foxy look suddenly infuriated Lucie. She had what she afterwards described to herself as a rush of blood to the head. Crimson, breast heaving, she flung out both arms, waving them rather like a small windmill.

"Well—I've changed my mind. I refuse to be co-operative. I've decided that it's nonsense. If Nat had wanted to marry you he would have asked you to long ago. I knew him long before you did . . . no . . ." she corrected herself a trifle sheepishly . . . "I didn't, but we were close friends all last summer and I understand him just as well as you do, if not better. My coming here confirmed his opinion that he didn't want to marry you. Now what he does about *me* is his affair. He can act and choose for himself. He doesn't want any coercion from us. *I'm* not going to interfere, and I'm not going to leave the way any clearer for you than for myself. If Nat stays at Keynwood, so shall I. I don't care what you say. And if you try to induce your mother to give me the sack, I shall go to the Head and tell him everything. I shan't be turned out. I've done my job, and I believe I've made a success of it. Everybody says so, anyhow. I won't have everything spoilt by your beastly jealousy . . ."

Lucie paused, choked, gasped for breath. She had never made such a long and impassioned speech in her whole life. She surprised herself and she stupefied Barbara who, with changing colour, stared and stared at her.

"Why, you—" began Barbara.

But Lucie was not prepared for any more. She turned and darted out of the room. Her heart thudded, she couldn't see very straight. Somehow she felt so extraordinarily angry. She kept gasping to herself.

'Nat, Nat, *Nat*. I don't care what anybody says. Or even what *you* say. I love you. And I believe that you love me. Once, you said so, "in your funny way". I'm not going to give up hope until I *die*!'

Down the stairs she ran, clutching at the banisters, trying to recover herself. Tea was being served in the common-room. In this new mood of wild rebellion and provocation, Lucie marched into the room and poured herself out a cup of tea from the big brown pot. She put in four lumps of sugar. She rarely liked her tea so sweet but she just went on dropping one lump after the other into the cup. This was noticed by Beryl Day. Berry was perched on the arm of a chair by the open window letting the sun shine on her. They hadn't seen enough of it lately.

She called out gaily to Lucie:

"Hey, you—you'll lose that nice little figure of yours if you go on like that."

"I don't care," said Lucie.

Berry stopped teasing and looked with some anxiety at the face of the young girl to whom she had grown truly attached. She had never seen Lucie look so hot and bothered before, she thought. Poor Lucie was inclined to take things too much to heart, in Berry's opinion.

'I used to be like her years ago,' Berry thought with some cynicism, 'but I've learned it doesn't pay. It's best to be a little hard and not let things hurt one too much . . .'

(Oh, she could say that and yet how badly she could still be hurt in her own life. She was always the giver, and there were so many 'takers' around.)

Lucie, alone of all the residents in the school whom Berry had ever known, had taken the trouble to be really sweet to her.

During one of the Geography classes this morning, Beryl had heard two of the pupils giggling over her nickname 'Horsey'. She ought to be used to it and usually she smiled grimly and didn't care. All little boys were horrors. One must just try to cram as much knowledge into their small mushy brains as possible. Such a limited few were really interested in the latitude or longitude of any country. Why worry about the name of the world's longest and widest river? That was the attitude of all but the few really intelligent pupils.

The nickname 'Horsey' had, especially today, brought home the fact which Beryl Day could not always face: that she was a plain woman with big teeth. Somehow it had made her feel extraordinarily lonely in that class of healthy, happy little boys. Now her frustrated maternal streak asserted itself. She slid off the chair, put down her cup, walked to Lucie and put an arm around the small waist which she so envied.

"What's the matter, ducky? You look thoroughly upset. Tell Berry."

And Lucie burst into tears and hid her face on Berry's ample bosom.

"Oh, Berry, I'm so miserable," she wept.

"Here," said Berry, hugging her, "something *is* wrong, you poor kid. This isn't at all like you. Come on up to my room and let's talk. Someone may come in here."

"No . . . I'm all right," began Lucie.

"Have a sip of that hot sweet tea and come up with me," insisted Berry.

So it happened that a few moments later Lucie found herself sitting on Berry's bed pouring out the whole story.

Perhaps she wouldn't have told Beryl Day about Nat if she hadn't been so upset by Barbie—and by her own torn emotions. But she was so tired of the fight which had reached such an impassioned pitch. She finished:

"Ought I to give in my notice, Berry, and get out before the Frierns fling me out, do you think?"

The Geography mistress had listened to the whole story in silence—an unusual silence for her. The dumpy little figure in the badly washed cotton dress and shapeless jersey, so familiar to Lucie, paced up and down the room. Berry smoked a cigarette, exhibiting no particular excitement, only shaking her head in sympathy now and again.

When Lucie had finished pouring out her heart, the older woman then had her say. She was not surprised. She had thought for some time that Lucie had a 'thing' about Nat Randall. Most of the women who met him seemed to fall for him, with the exception of Joanna Parrish who was just the odd one out and who didn't respond to his charm. But as for Barbara Friern—why, everybody at Keynwood was well aware that Barbie was crazy about Nat and all the more so because he didn't want more than the odd flirtation with her.

In reply to Lucie's question: "Do you think she really loves him?" Berry flicked the ash from her cigarette and said: "Love, my foot. That girl doesn't love anybody but herself. She's infatuated. He amuses and challenges her. She's tried to get 'em all here in turn, including Geoff. You know it. You needn't feel guilty about *her*."

"She hates me, Berry. If I don't leave of my own accord, she'll try and get me sacked."

"She may try, but I don't think she'll succeed. You've made your mark at Keynwood, my dear. The Head thinks the world of you. The boys love you. Of course they won't give you the sack and you'll be a fool if you leave just because of Miss Hoity-Toity Friern."

Lucie covered her face with her hands.

"But there's Nat . . . Nat doesn't want me any more than he wants Barbie."

"I wouldn't be too sure of that," said Berry. "I know Nat pretty well. He's been rather naughty about one or two girls and he's an incorrigible flirt, but there's a lot of good stuff in that young man. I believe he's got the sense to realise that you'd be the exact right wife for him. You have understanding and stability—they're the things that he needs. I think you should keep faith, and not be driven away from him, or from the school."

Lucie raised a flushed tearful face.

"You're very encouraging, Berry darling."

"Not without reason," said Berry in a gruff voice. She was more moved than she cared to admit by the sight of Lucie's tears and grief, and it was a long, long time since Beryl Day had heard anyone call her 'darling'. She bent and kissed one of the hot moist cheeks of the young girl and in the same gruff voice, said:

"Chin up, ducky. Don't let it get you down."

"Do *you* like Nat?" suddenly Lucie asked her.

"Of course I like him. I think he's madly attractive. If I were young and pretty I'd be scratching your eyes out in my own effort to get him," laughed Beryl. "But no man's going to propose to me and I know it. I'm sticking to my map of the world and my efforts to teach the rising generation."

"Well, I think you're a dear," said Lucie, "and you've been nice to me ever since I came."

She walked to the door but glanced back over her shoulder at the other woman.

"I can rely on you—" she began.

Berry held up a hand.

"Idiot. You know you can. Old Berry can keep her counsel, I assure you. Not a soul will ever hear from *me* about Nat and you."

Lucie felt better again. Berry's championship had done much to restore her confidence in herself. What she had said was only an echo of the things that Marta would have said, too.

For the rest of that day, Lucie tried to shed her cloak of depression, doubts and fears. She flung herself into her work. There seemed an extra lot of mending to do and she did it. Of course she was not quite sure about Barbara's attitude. Every time she met Stella Friern, Lucie wondered if she would be called in for 'a talk' and be asked to leave. But for the moment Barbara appeared to have said nothing about her personal affairs. She remained in her own bedroom for the rest of that day with a 'headache'. For this Lucie was thankful.

Nat had little to say to Lucie when they met for the evening meal. He was preoccupied and the subject of general conversation was the Head and his injury. Nat hardly addressed a word to either Berry or the little matron.

Geoff Mallow announced that he had been to see the invalid and thought he looked pale and shaken but not too bad. The school doctor had called. Stella said he was optimistic that the Headmaster would make a quick recovery. He was a man of courage and resilience.

Stella mentioned with more emotion than she usually displayed that the boys' delightful reception of her husband had meant a great deal to him. He kept referring to it.

The next few days were uneventful. Exams began. Pressure of work seemed to increase. The teaching staff, without their Head in action, found more than enough to do.

It was astonishing, Lucie thought, that she could live under the same roof as Nat, yet hardly ever see him. But she, too, was kept occupied. Soon it would be time for the sorting and packing to begin. The long summer vacation was in sight. She could hardly believe that she had been matron at Keynwood Hall School for a whole term.

The dreaded summons from the Frierns still did not come, but between the two girls a wall of ice had arisen. Neither spoke to the other. They completely avoided each other.

The evening meal in the Headmaster's dining-room began to be something of a nightmare to Lucie. Geoffrey and Berry were always ready to chat in a natural way. She could turn to them. But she remained painfully conscious of Nat's presence. He looked pale, strained and over-tired, she thought, and was obviously doing too much, what with his own examinations and end-of-term problems, and the work he was doing in Hugh Friern's place. After the first week home Mr. Friern did not recover quite as quickly as everybody had hoped. Ten days after the accident he was still in his own room with a fluctuating temperature and severe headaches.

On the one occasion when Lucie ran into Nat when by himself, he stopped but spoke only a few casual words. Lucie had to resort to day-dreaming and her own still unquenched faith in her love, in order to keep that flame alight. She certainly had no encouragement from *him*. A little bitterly, she decided that men seemed able to switch off their emotions like hot and cold taps. Work was the thing of paramount importance in their minds. She began to wonder if he had the slightest realisation of what she was going through.

There were nights when her pillow was wet with tears and her rest was sadly disturbed by hours of seeking a way out of her maze of trouble. She began to look forward to the holidays.

Dick's leave was ending. The German girl had given notice and Maggie would soon be alone and in need of help. She would go back to the little house in Hove for the rest of the summer. Back to the old heartache and inner loneliness—without Nat, without hope of Nat. How, she asked herself, could she really look forward to *that*? It was a devastating prospect.

Sometimes she envied the little boys she looked after. She wished she herself could be a screaming, laughing, carefree schoolgirl again. No use saying 'These are the best days of your life'. Yet it was true.

But it was a very unhappy Lucie who went about her work while the days rushed by toward the end of term.

25

Cᴀᴍᴇ the great day of good-byes.
    The school buzzed and hummed with excited voices
and the usual crowds and their activities through all the rooms
and corridors, and all the cars arriving to collect the boys for
the longest and best holiday of the year.

Lucie that morning was conscious of very mixed feelings.
She was relieved in a sense because she was going to get
away where she could not see Nat. Hope had almost vanished
now. He had said and done almost nothing to suggest that
she had any particular place in his life. He was just a friend.
His attitude was friendly, but vague, casual to the point of
breaking her heart. Better, perhaps, to get right away from
him again.

At least she would be glad to say good-bye to Barbie
Friern. The hostility between them was nothing short of
disagreeable.

The boys bade her good-bye obviously in high spirits, but
showing just enough affection to warm her heart.

"See you next term . . ." they all said.

And most of the mothers added:

"Thank you so much for all you've done, Matron. See you
next term."

But would they? That was the question Lucie could not
quite answer. She intended to go home and talk things over
with Maggie. When she was away from Nat she might be
able to decide whether or not she could face another term.

The Headmaster was up for the final day and being his
usual genial efficient self, looking none the worse for his
accident, except for a disfiguring plaster across his nose.

He was kind and complimentary when he said good-bye
to the little matron. He spoke, as Stella Friern did, with the
full belief that she would be returning to Keynwood.

"We'll expect you back on September 20th," he said.

Berry bade her farewell with reluctance.

"I shall miss you, little Lucie. I'm going to take my motor
coach tour around Scandinavia but when I come back I'll
come and call at your Hove house, if I may."

"Of course you can," said Lucie, "and thanks for all your kindness to me, Berry."

Berry whispered now:

"Any news for me?"

But Lucie turned red, then pale, and shook her head.

"Nothing. Not a word. I think it's all over."

Then she was caught up by another batch of parents. Sir Mark Finch asked especially to speak to her. With the shining-eyed and excited Jeremy, he talked to Lucie in the Headmaster's study.

The baronet had had a bright idea. He wanted to take his small son to Falmouth for three weeks. Sir Mark was keen on sailing. He had a motor boat down there. He also had a favourite 'pub'—The Rising Sun in St. Mawes. They would go to stay there. It would be a lovely healthy holiday for Jeremy but Mark wanted somebody to help look after the little fellow. It had suddenly struck Mark that as Jeremy was so devoted to the young Keynwood matron, she might go down to St. Mawes with them, and do a holiday governess job.

"Of course at a really good salary," Mark concluded with a smile.

Lucie could not help but be flattered, especially when young Finch tugged at her arm and said:

"Oh, Matron, *please* come. It would be smashing to have you."

"Smashing," echoed Sir Mark with a broad smile, "that's the word."

Lucie struggled with her thoughts.

Oh, if only she could forget Nat and just be uninhibited and fancy-free; how easily then she could have accepted this invitation. What a marvellous holiday it would be down in Cornwall in company with a man so delightful as Sir Mark— plus the 'Silver Cloud'—*and* the boat. Only the thought of Nat held her back. She made the stammering reply that she must think it over.

"That's all right," said Mark, "you know my London telephone number. I shan't be going down to Cornwall till next week. Just give me a ring."

Now the school was empty of boys. The last car had gone. Once more peace fell across Keynwood.

Slowly Lucie walked back into the common-room and stood

gazing bleakly around her, remembering the first day she had come here, and Nat's cool reception of her. Remembering, too, his kisses, his caresses, down there by the pool. *Where was he?* She wanted badly to see him and say good-bye, yet dreaded the moment. She went into the kitchen. Mrs. Egbert and Betty were drinking tea. Herta had already left in order to catch her plane to Copenhagen. She was flying back to Denmark. Her licence to work in England had expired but she had promised to send a new girl over to take her place.

"Well, thank goodness I don't have to cook for all those little so-and-sos for another eight weeks," said Mrs. Egbert.

Betty, cigarette between her lips, eyed Lucie and said:

"All over now, Matron, until the little weepers come back to weep their 'earts out."

Lucie said:

"Thanks for everything you've both done for me."

"Thank *you*," said Mrs. Egbert and Betty—Betty adding:

"You're by far the nicest matron we've ever had at Keyn-wood. Have a nice cuppa before you go."

But Lucie refused. She kept thinking, *where's Nat . . . I must see Nat.*

The last time she had set eyes on him he had been talking to the mother of the twins out in the drive.

She began to search the school-house but found no Nat, and now a horrible little fear seized her that he might have gone. Gone without even saying *good-bye*. She laughed to herself rather hysterically. That would be bad manners if nothing else . . .

With a sinking heart, she retraced her footsteps back to the main hall, meaning to go upstairs and pack her own trunk. She had ordered a taxi to take her to Horsham station later on and catch a train to Hove. There was still a lot for her to do before she could get away like the others. The last 'tidy round' in the boys' bedrooms, and the last laundry list to check.

Then she met Geoff Mallow.

"Ah! I've been looking for you. Like a fool it never entered my head until now that you would have a trunk and need to be taken to the station. I would drive you into Brighton but I've got a business date and I'm going up to town tonight."

'If only I wanted to see Geoff as much as I do Nat,' Lucie thought miserably. She said aloud:

"Jolly nice of you, Geoff, but I've already ordered a taxi."

"Shall I see you during the holidays?"

"You know I'll always be delighted if you'll come to my sister's house."

He looked down at her and added rather awkwardly:

"There's been such a rush lately, I haven't had much chance to ask you, but *are* you coming back next term?"

"I think so. I'm not sure," she answered, avoiding his gaze.

But after a moment, she could not refrain from blurting out the all-important question.

"Do you happen to have seen Nat?"

"Yes. Didn't he say good-bye to you? He dashed off about an hour ago."

Lucie stood still. She felt quite sick. She tried to speak brightly.

"Oh, did he? What was the hurry?"

"I'm not quite sure. He had a trunk call which seemed to excite him a great deal because he said he'd just had very important news and was rushing off to try and get a plane to Paris. He can have Paris. I prefer my English countryside."

Geoffrey talked on, but Lucie was no longer listening. She was conscious of only one fact: Nat had gone without saying good-bye to her and he had gone to Paris. That seemed a long, long way away. *Why* he had gone and in such a hurry she could not begin to guess. But she felt completely crushed.

She could be positive now, she told herself, that he did not care whether she lived or died. Possibly he had applied for some job on the Continent and had got it and was going over for an interview. That was what he seemed to want. To get abroad, away from them all—herself included.

Geoffrey saw the stricken look in the little matron's eyes and wondered, embarrassed and distressed, what he could do.

"Good-bye, Geoff, I must fly . . ." she said.

Then she was gone. Geoffrey raised his brows, shook his head and went his way feeling unhappy about the situation in general.

He might, he supposed, have asked Lucie to marry him. He almost liked her enough to forsake the bachelorhood to which he was sworn. He could imagine her making a charming wife. On the other hand he knew perfectly well that he would not make a charming husband. He was better living alone.

Some men could live alone and like it. Dedicated men like himself. Foolish to be tempted by a pair of beautiful eyes that looked as wounded as those of a stricken deer. Lucie's eyes. Foolish to be misled by pity for her into a proposal of marriage. Better stick to friendship and his flowers and birds.

Sighing, Geoffrey went his way.

For a moment Lucie lingered in the hall. She looked up at the stag's head; the proud noble head of an animal that had most certainly fought to the death rather than surrender. Once before during the term she had extracted a queer courage from the sight and thought of the stag. Now a bitter grief filled her heart as she stared up into the glassy, expressionless eyes.

'Poor noble creature. They got you in the end. Now life has got *me*. I feel as dead and as glassy-eyed as you look. You have my sympathy. Nat has murdered me. He ought to cut off my little head and hang it up beside yours . . .'

Her own stupid thoughts made her laugh. She was still laughing, while she finished the rest of her work in the school. Then she was in the taxi driving away from the school to Horsham station. Her eyes were dry although the lids burned and ached. The ache in her heart had become almost unbearable. She kept thinking:

'He might have said good-bye to me. Oh, he might have told me he was walking out . . .'

Feeling as though she were in a sad, endless dream from which she could not wake herself, she travelled home.

Timothy and baby Angela met her joyously.

"Good-oh! Auntie Lucie's home . . ." Tim greeted her with an affectionate hug.

Maggie came into the hall looking equally pleased.

"I've been missing Dick. It'll be lovely to have you back, Lucie."

"Grand to be back," said Lucie in a bright hard voice.

She helped the taxi driver bring in her trunk and carry it up to her room. After he had gone, Maggie said:

"You look hot and tired, duckie. I expect you've had a hellish lot to do getting all those boys off. I'm just going to give the children their supper, then we'll have ours, and a good natter."

Lucie was alone in her small bedroom. Familiar, yet strange to her after the long term at Keynwood in that other room.

She would be here for the next eight weeks, unless she cared to ring Sir Mark Finch and accept his invitation. When she had told Geoff Mallow about Cornwall, he had advised her to go. She would have a wonderful time, why not accept, he had said with his usual sound commonsense. Well, why not? she asked herself, now. It was all over with Nat. It must be. Why not join Sir Mark and Jeremy and be spoiled for a change.

But suddenly she gave a heart-broken little cry, flung off her coat and threw herself down on her bed in a storm of tears. Once again William Hazlitt's words crowded into her suffering mind:

> *'The barbed arrow is in my heart—I can neither endure it, nor draw it out; for with it flows my life's blood.'*

26

ONE week had passed.
Lucie began to feel that she had never left Maggie's house and taken that fateful and fatal job at Keynwood. She slipped back into the old routine: helping Maggie with the housework and minding the children.

On this particular Friday, because the weather was bright and warm she took the children by bus to Rottingdean. They intended to have a picnic lunch on the beach. Maggie had gone up to town on one of her rare days 'off', to meet a friend for lunch, and to shop. It was so wonderful to have her half-sister home to look after the children. Somebody she could entirely trust.

It was because Maggie was looking a trifle worn and weary, now that the German girl had gone that Lucie had decided not to accept Sir Mark's invitation to St. Mawes, but to stay at home. She couldn't bear the thought of spending that luxurious holiday with the Finchs while Maggie toiled with Tim and Angela, single-handed. In addition to this Maggie had said:

"If I thought it was the right thing, I'd make you go,

Lucie duckie, but I do feel it would be wrong if you think young Finch's father is in the least interested in you—seeing as how you are still so much in love with Nat."

To which she had added rather acidly:

"Although I wish to goodness you could wash Mr. Randall right out of your hair. This is the second time he's upset your life."

Lucie had argued hotly in defence of Nat.

"It's not his fault. It's mine. I pursued him. I made another mistake, but I won't make one a third time."

But not even Maggie knew what a week of blinding misery this had been for Lucie. On two separate occasions she wrote to the Frierns to tell them that she could not go back. She had felt she *could not* see Nat again day after day knowing that he cared so little for her. It would be too much. Yet each letter she had torn to pieces. Why, she did not know.

This morning her head ached and her spirits felt at zero. The children had been particularly trying—no doubt because of the hot weather. They were both spoiled, anyhow. Lucie had had Angela in a screaming fit and Tim grumbling because he could not stay in the water as long as he wanted to. Now, however, they were good at last, busy digging a sand-castle, because the tide was out. Lucie reclined with her back to a sun-baked wall, a book unopened on her lap, her eyes immeasurably sad behind her dark glasses.

Whenever she thought about Nat, it was with anguish, wondering why he had gone to Paris and if he ever remembered her existence.

She allowed her eyes to close for a few seconds, feeling the lids weighted, her slim body languid and tired. She looked like a child in her blue jeans and cotton shirt, with bare feet.

For a split second, she dozed off—yet still conscious of the fact that she must not really sleep because she had the children to watch. Then she heard her name:

"*Lucie!*"

She did not even bother to unclose her eyes, but answered: "Yes, Nat. I'm here, Nat . . ."

Of course it was a dream—one of those dreams she had had so often lately and from which she would awake with tears scalding her cheeks.

She heard footsteps on the shingle behind her and felt a touch on her hair.

"*Santa Lucia!*"

Now her eyes flashed open. She sprang up, her heart-beats jerking her to action and her whole body aflame. *He was here.* Here, standing before her. It was no dream. Nat, so familiar and debonair in well-remembered grey flannels. Nat, looking at her with a warmth and eagerness in his handsome eyes which she rarely remembered seeing, was actually here.

"Haven't I been clever to find you?" he asked with one of his mocking smiles.

She pushed the untidy hair back from a moist forehead and the man noted with tenderness the little human touch of vanity that made her take off her glasses and stuff them in the pocket of her jeans. Her eyes had grown huge with astonishment and pleasure.

"Oh, Nat!" she exclaimed, "where on *earth* have you sprung from?"

"Paris to London by plane. London to Brighton by car. Maggie's house—and a 'daily' to tell me that Mrs. Callow is in London and Miss Reed with the kids at Rottingdean. So here I am. I've left my car up in the car park where there's a darned awful crowd and I almost couldn't get in."

Lucie found herself gasping. The shock of seeing Nat here in Rottingdean was at once painful and glorious. She could hardly believe her own eyes. He threw himself down on the shingle, took a handkerchief from his pocket, wiped his forehead, then began to divest himself of his coat.

"I'm roasted. For heaven's sake sit down, sweetie, and talk to me for a minute, then I'll take you somewhere to get cool and have some tea."

"But we haven't had lunch yet."

"Then I'll take you and the kids to lunch."

"But I've got a picnic here—" she began.

"Oh, no you don't—I detest picnics. We'll find a nice cool hotel and eat frightful English food, but at least I can get a drink in a hotel. Picnics are not my line."

"Oh, Nat." She began to laugh helplessly, shaking her head, and sat down beside him, thankful that the children were busy and leaving her alone, and that this part of the beach, at least, was not too crowded.

"Now let me tell you all that's been happening," he said.

"First of all why did you rush off to Paris without saying good-bye to me?"

"I tried to find you but couldn't and it was a question of minutes to spare if I wanted to get my plane."

"But why—"

He interrupted that question. He would tell her everything if she would just sit still and listen, he said. So Lucie heard the real reason why he had rushed off with such apparent callousness and not been in touch with her since.

He had received a telephone call from a hotel in Paris on that day of departure from the school. Uncle Henry had been staying there in a party which included the girl he intended to marry. But Uncle Henry never lived to contract his marriage, Nat explained to Lucie. He was found dead in bed. He had had a heart attack and the erstwhile fiancée, who knew of Nat's existence, had telephoned to him to go over there immediately. It had taken a week for Nat to get affairs straightened out and poor Uncle Henry buried, after which Nat returned to London to be told by Uncle Henry's lawyers that he was sole heir. He had, in fact, inherited the very nice round sum of thirty thousand pounds.

"The fiancée's bad luck was my good fortune," said Nat as he smoked his cigarette, and blinked at the sun-lit sea. "I must admit that I never expected it. Now when I most need it I have some capital. A chance to start out on my own—at last."

"Oh, Nat, I'm tremendously glad for you, although sorry for poor Uncle Henry," exclaimed Lucie.

His gaze returned to her.

"So you see, my dear, I've scarcely had a moment in which to get in touch with you."

Lucie looked down at the shingle and dug a little circle with her fingers rather nervously.

"I don't really see why you should have bothered to, if it comes to that."

"There was every reason, which is why I've come straight here from the airport today."

An imp of mischief made her grin at him.

"You might well have been told that I was in Cornwall with Sir Mark Finch."

"That's what I was afraid of," said Nat.

"Afraid of!" jeered Lucie. "*You!*"

"Yes, afraid," he repeated the word seriously.

"Why?"

"Because I didn't want you to go down to Cornwall with the noble baronet and start anything."

"Start what?"

"The sort of thing that I hope you'll start with me, my dear little sainted one."

Her cheeks went fiery red. Her heart galloped.

"I don't know what you mean."

"I mean that I think little Finch's papa entertained the bright idea that once he was free you might become little Finch's step-mama."

"Well, what of it?" she asked, her lips dry.

"Lucie, don't be difficult. You know that I love you. I told you so the last time that we met."

She felt for a moment as though sun and sea and the world revolved around her; she reached such dizzy heights.

"You did tell me you loved me 'in your funny way', Nat, but I didn't pay much attention to it."

"Well, you'll have to start paying some attention to it now. Once I got to Paris and had time to sort myself out, I realised beyond all shadow of doubt that I was in love with you in a not-so-funny way. Now do you understand?"

"Then Barbie Friern—"

"We won't talk about Barbie. That's all over. And I admit I'm ashamed of the affair."

Lucie made no answer. Nat looked at her small flushed face long and earnestly. Yes, he thought, he was sure this time how much she had grown to mean to him, and that he could not do without her. He had dreamed about her in Paris. On the flight back to England he had felt that he was flying expressly back to *her*. He had grown to love this small sweet slip of a girl, who had such a lot of courage and character, with all his soul. She held a place in his heart that none of the other women he had ever known—no matter how glamorous—could touch.

He took her hand and put it against his lips kissing it softly and gently.

"*Santa Lucia*," he said, "my darling, you may be a saint and I may be a devil. Perhaps it's a curious mixture. It might also mean that a union of the two might be a brilliant success. I want you to marry me."

Now in truth the world and time, itself, stood still for Lucie. It was an almost unbearably poignant moment of triumph, reaching the long end of the road that she had been following so desperately. Nat added:

"I've got it all worked out, my sweet. I'll have to go back to Keynwood for one more term rather than let old Hugh down. If he doesn't want my fiancée there as the matron then you'll have to chuck your job. He'll have to lose one of us. But we'll have a nice Christmas wedding, and a wonderful honeymoon on the Continent where we'll spend a little of poor Uncle Henry's money together, and meanwhile I'm going to look for a school of my own. Somebody once said I was a born teacher and would hate to do nothing, and it's true. We'll run a prep school and you'll be the headmaster's wife instead of the matron, and all the little boys will adore you, and I'll have to keep you away from the fathers in case one of them, like Sir Mark, tries to whisk you away from under my nose because you're so young and charming."

Lucie shook her head.

"Nat, Nat, don't go on! . . . it isn't true, any of it. You're making it all up."

"I most certainly am not. I admit it may all seem sudden and a complete *volte-face*, but I swear to you that I *knew*, once I got to Paris, that it had to be you, my darling child."

Now she could not see Tim and Angela digging their sand-castle, because her tears blinded her. She felt a handkerchief being pushed into one of her hands.

"Dry them, darling," said Nat. "There's nothing to cry about now."

"Yes, there is," she said angrily, "I'm so terribly, madly happy."

"Commend me to women for being the most charming and and illogical creatures. Why cry for happiness?"

"I hate logic."

"Sure you don't hate me?"

"I think I did when we broke up at Keynwood and I thought you'd run out on me."

"What a frightful fellow I must be. How can you love or want me?"

"Women seem to love and want you—lots of women."

"And I want only one. You, my *Santa Lucia*."

She flung his handkerchief back at him. Her wet eyes were shining brilliantly, her lips trembling into a radiant smile.

"Nat, *Nat* . . ."

"Shall we go and lunch at 'The Harpsichord' and eat John's chicken dish made with wine and cream and mushrooms and pineapple?" He asked, smiled reminiscently and lifted the small hand that had thrown the handkerchief back to him. He put his lips against the soft moist palm.

"Yes, oh *please* . . . let's," she cried joyfully.

"We'll go to Rome for our honeymoon . . . find that little street of the painted shrine."

"Yes, oh, yes."

He pulled her suddenly close to him.

"You know, Lucie, you're lovelier and sweeter than any matron of any school has any right to be. You must definitely resign from Keynwood. You can take care of only one horrible boy in future—myself."

"You aren't horrible!" she protested with indignation.

He smoothed the hair back from her forehead.

"How forgiving women are. You make me feel very humble. But I swear I'm right in thinking that we are going to be very happy together."

Lucie closed her eyes as he kissed her, hard on the mouth, and when the kiss ended, whispered:

"You are right, Nat darling. Absolutely, gorgeously right!"

Denise Robins From Coronet

- [ ] 19473 1 THIS SPRING OF LOVE — 35p
- [ ] 01893 3 WE TWO TOGETHER — 35p
- [ ] 02921 8 THE STORY OF VERONICA — 35p
- [ ] 10882 7 WAIT FOR TOMORROW — 35p
- [ ] 02259 0 TO LOVE AGAIN — 35p
- [ ] 12948 4 THE CRASH — 35p
- [ ] 16218 X A PROMISE IS FOREVER — 35p
- [ ] 14877 2 LOVE AND DESIRE AND HATE — 35p
- [ ] 16083 7 A LOVE LIKE OURS — 35p
- [ ] 01264 1 MAD IS THE HEART — 35p
- [ ] 16204 X SWEET CASSANDRA — 35p
- [ ] 18605 4 ALL FOR YOU — 30p
- [ ] 01065 7 I SHOULD HAVE KNOWN — 30p
- [ ] 15084 X THE UNLIT FIRE — 30p
- [ ] 15110 2 SHATTER THE SKY — 30p
- [ ] 02795 9 THE STRONG HEART — 30p

All these books are available at your bookshop or news-agent, or can be ordered direct from the publisher. Just tick the titles you want and fill in the form below.

Coronet Books, P.O. Box 11, Falmouth, Cornwall.
Please send cheque or postal order. No currency, and allow the following for postage and packing:
1 book—10p, 2 books—15p, 3 books—20p, 4-5 books—25p, 6-9 books—4p per copy, 10-15 books—2½p per copy, 16-30 books—2p per copy, over 30 books free within the U.K.
Overseas—please allow 10p for the first book and 5p per copy for each additional book.

Name ....

Address ....

....